THE HARTLEY COLLIERY
DISASTER, 1862

AT REST

This beautiful Memorial—recently restored—is to be found in the churchyard at Earsdon. Inscribed on its four sides are the names of the 204 men
and boys who were lost in the Hartley Disaster.

PHOTO BY J. C. CURRY

THE HARTLEY COLLIERY
DISASTER, 1862

by

JOHN ELLIOTT McCUTCHEON

WITH A FOREWORD BY

The Rt. Hon. LORD ROBENS of Woldingham, P.C.,
Chairman, National Coal Board.

E. McCUTCHEON
2 Ambleside Avenue . Seaham . Co. Durham
1 9 6 3

Two Press comments on the Hartley Disaster :

So dire a misfortune attended by such horror of circumstance is not recorded in the history of mining.

Illustrated London News, 25th January, 1862.

It is a spectacle and a thought to possess the mind of a nation. The worst horror of the lowest dungeon and the tyrant's oubliette was here done on the largest scale on meek and innocent sons of toil. They had aroused no suspicion, penned no libel, breathed no heresy, whispered no watchword, offended no Bourbon, scandalized no inquisition ; yet here they were, a hundred Ugolinos and their sons, confronting one another in the jaws of a living death with a mutual embrace and a common hope of Heaven.

Times, 24th January, 1862.

FOREWORD

The history of the mining industry is the history of the rise of Britain to the pinnacle of industrial supremacy in the world. A Britain which became the world's workshop, a world in which the pound was the King of the Earth and the dollar a mere débutante. Britain's riches and greatness were built on coal. And while her vast merchant fleet ploughed its way throughout the Seven Seas, and ships nosed their way into foreign ports, big and small, unloading their merchandise, a vast army of men, and indeed in the early days, women and children too, toiled in the bowels of the earth, wresting from Nature the energy that lay in those black seams of coal. The rise and fall of the British Empire, the creation of a Commonwealth of Nations, bound together by nothing more tangible than a desire to keep together, and to respect the Crown, has been told over and over again. But the story of the men of the mines has to be found in the recollection of the old men, the poems of the pitmen poets, the songs of the older mining districts. But few, all too few, of the colourful stories of the lives of the miners and the communities in which they lived in comparative isolation from the rest of the population, have been recorded.

John McCutcheon in this book gives us an authentic, awe-inspiring pen picture of the Hartley disaster. Two hundred and four men and boys paid with their lives for the hard lesson that had to be learned that a coal mine needs two shafts. Within a few months of their mass burial this became the law of the land. Today the scene of those anxious, terror-stricken days, six days of heroism, striving, heartbreak and grief, is difficult to find. But John McCutcheon found it, as he searched diligently to find all the facts of those six days when, for the people of Hartley, the world stood still. In these pages he brings to life the events of one hundred years ago. He uses words as an artist uses his paint. The deep colours, the broad strokes, the highlights, the shade and the dark are all there. With them the great welter of human

v

emotion from the broken hearts of the womenfolk to the anger of the crowd. Now he has completed a trilogy. His **Troubled Seams** (1955), and **A Wearside Mining Story** (1960), recount mining events in his native Durham. Now over the River Tyne from Northumberland comes the graphic true story of Hartley.

It was in the autumn of 1945 that my dear old friend, Alderman Dan Dawson, known throughout the county as Dan to young and old alike, took me to Earsdon Church Yard and showed me the monument to the dead of the Hartley Colliery disaster. I remember the awful shock I felt as I stood there and read the names of whole families, fathers, their adult sons and young children. That memory has stayed with me ever since, and when, fifteen years later John McCutcheon told me he was contemplating writing the story of Hartley, I urged him to do it. And here it is. A tribute to the mining industry, by a man from mining stock, himself a miner in his early days. A fascinating story strongly told of an event which compelled Parliament to change the law, which drew the attention of a whole nation to the men who work in mines, and drew forth the personal grief and anxiety of a widowed Queen.

John McCutcheon has done a great service in writing the story of Hartley. I commend it to all who are interested in the growth of industrial Britain, and the part the mining industry played in it.

ROBENS.

Woldingham,
Surrey.
February, 1963.

PREFACE

Some two years ago I received a letter addressed to me from the Aged Miners' Homes, Wingate, County of Durham. It was from a Mr. Ralph Lee, a retired miner.

Mr. Lee had, over many years, made an intensive study of mining history, and had acquired a number of books on the subject. Some of these he now proposed to dispose of, and, having read my **Troubled Seams,** was kind enough to think I might care to take a few of his books.

As a result of this letter, I went over to Wingate one Sunday afternoon, and after a most enjoyable chat came away with a few volumes, one of which I was delighted to see was about the Hartley Colliery Disaster.

Now I was of course already familiar with the Hartley story. How could it be otherwise to anyone with the slightest acquaintance with mining history? I had read several accounts of the Disaster including that remarkable narrative in the form of a novel written by my friend Harold Heslop and entitled **The Earth Beneath.** But I had not previously seen this particular book, obtained that Sunday afternoon, with its full and authoritative report of that tragic event.

As I read and re-read the book, the Hartley Disaster, in all its vivid reality, took possession of me. I thereupon decided that it was high time the gripping story was re-told and resolved to apply myself to the task. Taking the book obtained from Ralph Lee as the nucleus of my tale, I embarked upon a wider research which involved much study and many journeys until there was evolved the book which is here presented to my readers.

In talking over my project here and there, I discovered the existence of a wide and sincere interest in the theme. Moreover, I learned that the essence of the Hartley lament had percolated down in mining families, instilled, like an intravenous drip from father to son, as a treasured family tradition to be cherished in remembrance.

An illustration of this occurred as follows : In the course of my researches I renewed contact with a friend, Mr. William Forrest, who left Seaham where he was manager of the Vane Tempest Colliery, to become Group Agent for some pits near Hartley in Northumberland. Before I visited his home in Morpeth last summer, in response to his invitation to talk about Hartley, he wrote a letter to me which contained the following observations which I feel might be multiplied in many Northern homes :—

> When I was a small boy, my grandfather used to tell me about the Disaster, and I think his father had helped in the rescue operations. The sketch of the broken beam used to hang on the wall in my grandfather's house . . .

That simply-worded statement illustrates the great hold which the Hartley story had for two or three generations after the event.

Another example of this interest in Hartley was revealed to me when, in May 1961, I received a letter from someone—a stranger to me—living in Lancashire. It was from a Mr. W. Anderson, a colliery manager, residing at Parbold, near Wigan. He spoke appreciatively of my two books, one of which he had discovered "on the shelves of Wigan Public Library".

In the course of his letter he happened to say that one of his forbears had worked as an overman "at the ill-fated Hartley Pit" but fortunately had left there prior to the Disaster. In my reply I noted the coincidence of his remark about Hartley since my next book concerned that very subject. Here is an extract from the next letter he wrote me :

> I am looking forward to the publication of your book about the Hartley Disaster. My grandfather had a print showing the broken beam which was framed and hung over his kitchen mantelpiece for more than fifty years.

Perhaps pictures of the broken beam no longer hang on cottage walls. But it is, nevertheless, true to say that the memory of the calamity lingers on.

For whatever changes the years may bring, the fact remains that the Hartley Disaster is still "unparalleled" in mining history. Hartley was dramatic, it epitomized in one great event the whole colossal suffering, sacrifice and heroism which has characterised so much of the mining story since the working of coal began some ten centuries ago.

JOHN E. McCUTCHEON.

2 Ambleside Avenue,
Seaham,
Co. Durham.
May, 1963.

ACKNOWLEDGMENTS

Much assistance has been rendered by many friends and well-wishers in the compilation of this work, and my thanks are due to the following :—

Lord Robens, not only for the Foreword here given, but also for his letter of encouragement concerning this project written to me in December 1961 ; Mr. W. R. Blyton, M.P., for verification of relevant material in the Library of the House of Commons ; Mr. Sam Watson, General Secretary, Durham Area N.U.M. ; Mr. Lawrence Scollen, Records Officer, Durham Area N.U.M. ; Mr. W. G. Innerd, of the Newcastle Central Reference Library ; Mr. J. T. Shaw, Director, and Mr. E. Kirtley, Deputy Director, Sunderland Libraries ; Mr. F. Rutherford, Librarian, Literary and Philosophical Society, Newcastle ; Mr. E. J. Clark, Durham County Librarian and his Deputy, Mr. R. N. Dixon ; Mr. A. Walker of the North of England Institute of Mining and Mechanical Engineers ; the proprietors of the 'Illustrated London News' for permission to reproduce the graphic sketches of the Disaster scenes ; Mr. C. Cowley, Editor, 'Sunderland Echo' ; my printer, Mr. J. Greenwood, and his son, Fred, for their part in our continued happy relationship in this work.

Individual help has been readily given by Mr. W. Forrest, Mr. Haswell Alder, Mr. J. O. Shepherd, Mr. W. E. Hume, Mr. Sam Wilson, Miss E. Garrigan, and Mr. Ralph Lee. A special word of thanks is due to my friend Jim Curry for again co-operating with such excellent photographs. The fact that he went from Seaham to Earsdon in Northumberland especially to get me the photographs of the Hartley Memorial there, speaks for itself concerning the degree of his friendly collaboration. Finally, I am grateful to Miss D. L. Chambers, and Mrs. Julia Wilson, for correcting the proofs, and to my wife, for her forbearance concerning my fugitive withdrawal from company at all hours in pursuance of this compelling labour of love.

J.E.M.

CONTENTS

ILLUSTRATIONS

PART ONE

An Event Unparalleled

Chapter 1

" SO DIRE A MISFORTUNE . . . "

The Hartley Disaster is an event unparalleled in mining history. The tragedy occurred on the 16th January, 1862, in the tiny colliery village of Hartley in Northumberland. A word or two might suffice to indicate the immediate cause of it all, but what volumes would be needed fully to relate the great human story which followed in its wake.

The beam of the pumping engine which was poised over the pit-head, and weighed 42 tons, suddenly snapped in two, half of it crashing down the pit shaft whereby the miners below were entombed.

Despite the untiring efforts of a gallant band of would-be rescuers who toiled while the whole country "waited and watched and hoped" for their success, no less than 204 men and boys lost their lives. Three of a batch of eight men coming up in the cage at the time were saved as by a miracle.

So great was the blow which savagely struck this pit village that only 34 workmen connected with the colliery (fortunately not in the pit at the time) remained to mourn the fate of their fellow men.

The disastrous extent of the accident, its unique character, the nation-wide concern which it evoked, the whole concentrated tension and drama of the sad event, made "The Hartley Disaster" the talking point in pit, pub, club and chapel, indeed everywhere where men foregathered, for many a long day thereafter.

But time which has a way of healing wounds and concealing scars also blurs, often blissfully, the memory of the bitterest experience. So it is that with the growing up of new generations, this story, once so potent in the telling, has gradually lost its original freshness and personal intimacy and has become a faint echo of long ago.

If the truth of this was realised fifty years ago, how much more so now, one hundred years after the disaster !

15

Fifty years ago a responsible committee set about the task of placing on permanent record a first-hand and authoritative account of the disaster. This resulted in a wonderfully impressive and well-authenticated publication entitled **Memoir of the Hartley Colliery Accident and Relief Fund** which was prepared at the request of the General Committee of the Fund and edited by T. E. Forster. The work, which tells the story in the words of those who were actually present at the scene of the disaster, has been the main source book of the present writer's researches into this historic event.

The need for this **Memoir** of 1912 is summed up by its Editor in these words :

> Fifty years have now passed since the accident happened and but few outward signs of the old colliery remain at Hartley. The Shaft, in which the cause of the calamity, the half of the broken beam, still lies buried, is marked by a stone wall surrounding it in which the date stone of the old pumping engine house has been inserted, while some of the old work shops may yet be seen standing on the old pit-heap to the north. Beyond this there is little to remind the onlooker of the drama which was enacted here in those bleak January days half a century ago. Of the little band of sinkers and viewers and doctors who worked so unflinchingly and devotedly through so many weary hours, few, if any, are left. Years have told their accustomed tale, and though there are not many of the inhabitants of the district who have not heard of the Hartley accident, there are comparatively few remaining who can remember its grim realities or can have anything more than a vague knowledge of its story.

That was written fifty years ago. How much more necessary is it, for the story to be re-told to-day, one hundred years after the event.

A question arises here. Why, oh why is there so little literature available on these episodes of which the history of coal-mining is so full ? It is not only the historians of the past who have ignored them; even the literature of our own day manages to avoid to a large extent, references to these stories of coal with all their drama. As I have said elsewhere, Sidney Webb estimated that up to the year 1921 no less than one hundred thousand miners had been lost in the pits of Britain. It is common knowledge that of this number there were many

16

GENERAL VIEW OF THE HARTLEY PIT-HEAD

PHOTO-COPY BY J. C. CURRY

THE FLOODING OF A PIT

This picture illustrates the kind of trouble which frequently happened at Hartley many years ago. It led eventually to the installation of a powerful pumping engine with a great beam. A letter written in 1765 said . . .

" . . . Hartley Colliery, drowned for the time being, along with six poor men, three boys and five Galloways" (pit-ponies).

Picture from Simonin's "Mines and Miners" (1868). PHOTO-COPY BY J. C. CURRY

THE BROKEN BEAM

The Half of the Broken Beam which remained in the Engine House.

THE PIT CAGE (before and after the accident)

This cage was coming up the shaft with 8 men (4 on each deck) when the broken cast-iron beam (21 tons) came crashing down. Three men escaped from the wrecked cage as by a miracle.

instances of distressing calamities (each with its own by-product of outstanding heroism) amounting to major disasters of which Hartley is but one significant example. And yet, how lacking is the literature concerning them !

Recently I picked up a new book which I felt sure would mention the Hartley Disaster. This book, quite a good one, published in 1961, is entitled **Great True Stories of Tragedy and Disaster** by E. V. Corbett. Not only was Hartley overlooked, but there was not even a mention, so far as I could see, of a mining disaster. The Preface assures us that "Many hundreds of volumes have been searched in compiling this anthology of disasters . . . The collection ranges from the time of Nero to the end of 1959. It includes stories of fire, explosion, volcanoes and earthquakes, storms and floods; of plague, intrigue and massacre, of sea, air and railway accidents and disastrous episodes of the Second World War. They provide both drama on the grand scale and instruction".

Not a word about our coal-mines. Our mines which have levied such toll on human life and which have meant so much in the building of Britain's greatness.

This, surely, proves my point. Not only does Corbett's anthology fail to notice mining disasters, but also it seems, the "many hundreds of volumes" which were searched in its compilation. English literature's neglect of that side of our national story is not only a serious omission, it is a scandalous injustice and an insult to generations of our people who have bravely given so much in blood and sweat to the making of our heritage.

Why should Hartley be considered worthy of ranking high in any catalogue of our national disasters ? Perhaps the best answer to this question would be to quote the contemporary writers who gave their own definite evaluations of the historical significance of the Hartley Disaster :

Records of colliery disasters go back for centuries [but] of all the catastrophes which have occurred probably none has attracted such universal attention and sympathy as that which took place at Hartley Colliery on 16th January, 1862. The unique character of the accident leading to the suspense which continued for a period of six days and nights during which heroic efforts were being made by Mr. Coulson and his gallant band of sinkers to rescue the entombed men and boys, stirred the whole country as it waited and watched and hoped for the success of their untiring struggles.

—T. E. Forster.

No acts ever witnessed in the annals of the nineteenth century will outshine such as these. They deserve to be recorded on the eternal page of history as an honour to the men and the age which produced them.

—T. Wemyss Reid.

Here then, this fearful tragedy is being played out. Years hence this place will have a terrible interest in the eyes of all . . . A grim battle for life and death is going on here.

—T. Wemyss Reid.

So dire a misfortune attended by such horror of circumstance is not recorded in the history of mining.

—"Illustrated London News", 25th January, 1862

Those estimates of Hartley speak for themselves.

Thomas Burt, M.P., D.C.L., Pitman and Privy Councillor, for fifty years a leader of the Northumberland Miners (most of that time as their General Secretary) refers to the Hartley Disaster in his **Autobiography.**

At the time of the disaster, Burt was a coal hewer at Choppington Colliery, not far away. Many of those lost were friends of his, and he was soon at the pit-heap offering his services. This is what he has to say :—

In the melancholy annals of mining accidents Hartley stands alone. Never before had anything similar occurred, nor has there been anything of the kind since. The tragic event produced a profound sensation throughout the country and throughout the civilised world, and it cast a grim shadow over the whole district. I knew many of the workmen at Hartley though I had no relatives among them.

I was early on the scene—one of the thousands who felt the keenest sympathy and who would have been but too glad to help had help been possible. As is usual on such occasions, heroic efforts were put forth by brave volunteer workers who could be had in any number, under the guidance of the most capable and skilful mining engineers. All in vain. For the first few days hopes of rescue were indulged in, but as day followed day, it became only too apparent that the imprisoned miners were doomed to a lingering, painful death. Two hundred and four valuable lives were lost.

Of the contemporary reporters of the Hartley scene none has moved the present writer more than the account given by T. Wemyss Reid (later Sir Wemyss Reid). A reporter on the staff of the "Newcastle Daily Journal", he kept constant vigil at the pit-head throughout the period of the disaster. His on-the-spot reporting is graphic in the extreme, reading like despatches from a battle front, and he gives the impression of being somehow aware of the historical significance of the unique tragedy which fate had destined him to chronicle.

At the behest of many friends and in order to assist the Relief Fund his despatches were collected and published soon after the disaster, which work was fully reprinted and incorporated in the above-mentioned **Memoir** published in 1912.

In the Preface to the earlier work he modestly disclaims any literary merits for the publication but rightly says that "No other history which may be written of this sad catastrophe can be as fresh and as faithful as this one, rude and imperfect as it is".

The present writer takes the liberty, in later chapters, of quoting Reid's account at length because of its first-hand knowledge, its insight and its authenticity. During that week of crisis "Our own Correspondent" was on the job night and day. Day after day his despatches are headed "Midnight" or "3 a.m." or "5 a.m." or "Noon"—all hours of the day and night. Did this chronicler never sleep ? In the Preface to his earlier work he writes explaining the conditions under which his narrative was written :

It was written under circumstances which effectually prevented any attempt being made at fine or elegant writing. Some portions of the story were jotted down on the pit-heap at midnight, when the bitter cold hardly allowed the writer to hold his pencil in his hand and when the falling snow half obliterated all he had written. Others were hastily scrawled to catch a morning train after a weary night's watch, when it was almost impossible to keep the sleepy eyes open, or to concentrate the drowsy mind upon the matter in question.

19

The whole history was written amidst hurry and excitement of which the reader can, happily, have no conception.

Reid goes on to say that rather than re-write his story to give it more polish, he prefers to let his "fresh and faithful" account go just as it was scribbled at the mouth of the Hartley pit shaft.

And what—as if it were possible to summarize such an epic in a page ! — are one's own impressions of that astonishingly memorable week of January, 1862, after much reading and reflection ?

It was a week unforgettable by any standard. It was a week of reasonable hope; it was a week of black despair. For never in the whole history of such operations was work beset by so many infuriating frustrations as was this at Hartley.

There were indeed times soon after the men were "barred-in" when the rescuers from above heard the shouts, albeit faintly, of the victims below, and when "jowling" signals passed between both anxious communicants. Evidence was later forthcoming to show how some of the entombed men had laboured at the bottom-end of the shaft obstruction in their frantic effort to assist their own deliverance. But despite the maddening and tantalising nearness over that barrier in the shaft (a mere score or so of yards) a full week elapsed ere contact was actually made and the dreadful truth, "a vast Golgotha", was made known.

But what a week ! It was a week in which only two men at a time could work in two hour shifts having to labour in continuous succession the clock round in that cramped hole in the bowels of the earth that was the shaft; it was a week in which these workmen toiled suspended on ropes like acrobats with water pouring down upon them and debris falling from the shaft sides, and with, in the later stages, mine gas overwhelming them and causing their hasty withdrawal to the surface of the pit, where they themselves, the would-be rescuers, lay like corpses on the ground until the waiting doctors brought them back to life. And then, ere long, these same brave men would be back in the shaft continuing the battle with time—and death. What a week indeed !

20

It was a week of unending drama and crises, a week in which a tiny colliery village became the centre of national attention, its humble women-folk grief-stricken and tragic, receiving personal letters from the Queen of the Realm. It was a week of false rumour, wild speculation and invading multitudes of sightseers; a week of mass meetings, of on-the-spot conferences of pit officials, of pit-heap prayer meetings and open-air hymn-singing sessions, of endless emotional scenes, of demands for information and report, of individual manifestations of hysteria because of the agonizing suspense in which more than one demented relation threatened to jump down the pit shaft; a week of official explanations and pacifying assurances from a pit-head platform, a week whose macabre climax saw the arrival of a mountain of coffins, brought in a convoy of carts; coffins in such number that a special railway train was also commissioned to carry them; coffins which, on the day of the big burial were to be borne in a funeral procession four miles long !

And throughout this incredible week there was one constant factor. It was like a sadly monotonous undertone ever-present in a tragically moving symphony. It was the haunting presence, there around the pit-head, of the ranks of waiting relatives, women for the most part, white-faced and watchful, waiting in the cold grey half-light of each new day, waiting in the day-time while the feeble January sun made of the pit-head a sinister silhouette; waiting in the long watches of the night like alabaster ghosts in shawls, faintly discernible by the fitful flames from the braziers of burning coal, which did little, however, to counter the bitter mid-winter winds which blew in from the nearby North Sea. Winds which eventually, brought with them a white mantle of snow wherewith, providentially, to drape and enshroud the stark and brutal reality which the Hartley Pit enfolded in its bosom.

Such a week in our mining annals is surely deserving of thoughtful and respectful remembrance.

Chapter 2

THE HARTLEY PITS, OLD AND NEW

The name of Hartley is of great significance in the history of coal mining. From whatever point of view we consider the matter, whether it be from that of the antiquity of its coal-mining operations, its pioneering of new mining techniques, or the ultimate tragedy of its final chapter in which the New Hartley Hester Pit became the tomb for two hundred and four human souls, the name of Hartley must surely live.

Moreover the untiring efforts of the small band of heroes who, in the shaft, battled on for a week in appalling conditions to rescue the entombed men, ever hoping, ever struggling, but never succeeding in their great quest—that heroism is written in letters of fire which must also survive for all time.

First, a word about the Old Hartley Pits. According to "The History of Northumberland", Vol. 8 (issued by the Northumberland County History Committee) records of coal mines at Hartley go back as far as 1291, although these were, doubtless, small outcrop pits worked for local supply. Coal was being worked in the district by the Prior and Convent of Brinkburn at the time of the Dissolution, and this was afterwards leased by the Crown to Sir Ralph Delaval in 1596. Before this time salt pans, which greatly stimulated coal production, had been established at Hartley and their produce shipped at Blyth.

Some time later another Sir Ralph Delaval (grandson of the above) developed the property considerably. He built a pier at Hartley Pans, or Seaton Sluice, as it was afterwards called, and under his guidance the coal trade expanded.

The pits at this period were situated near the coast in the vicinity of Seaton Sluice where the three main seams—the High Main, the Yard, and the Low Main—were reached in shallow depths which rose towards the sea. This meant their development

22

was attended with difficulty owing to the heavy feeders of water which, from time to time, overcame the "rag and chain" pumps then in use.

In 1764 a new entrance was opened into the harbour at Seaton Sluice. This was cut through the solid rock to the east of the old approach and was looked upon as one of the greatest engineering feats of the day, in consequence of which more business was brought to the pits and Hartley Coal was held in high esteem in the trade.

Some indication of the importance of this coal producing area may be gathered from the fact pointed out by C. U. Nef ("Rise of the British Coal Industry, Vol. 2, p. 353) that the shipments of coal from Hartley and Blyth in 1799 amounted to 110,812 tons.

Moreover, the Hartley district was soon to the fore in the matter of mining technique. The Hartley pits pioneered the use of the revolutionary method then described as "drawing coals by fire", i.e., the raising of steam in coal-fired boilers for lifting the corves of coal up the shaft instead of adhering to the old method of horse-gin operation.

A new "fire-engine" designed by William Brown (at that time the greatest authority on pumping engines in the district) was set to work in 1760, and the year 1763 saw the introduction of a steam winding engine, the invention of Joseph Oxley of Ford.

Despite mechanical improvements, however, danger was ever-present. The workmen of Hartley, says Askham in his book The Gay Delavals "lived in a fearful world of fire-damp, choke-damp, the creeps and death by drowning".

With regard to the latter reference to "death by drowning" an interesting letter is quoted in The Gay Delavals. The Delavals were a powerful Northumberland family owning land and coal mines, whose reign of power ended when the last legitimate male Delaval was carried to his rest in the year 1814.

Captain Nethercott, who appears to have had some say in the local colliery management at Hartley, wrote to the absent Sir John Delaval about the flooding of the Hartley Pit which took place in 1765. This flooding caused the loss of several lives —men, boys and pit ponies. The letter ran as follows :

> Little did I dream when I had the honour to approach you last in the epistolary way of the melancholy catastrophe which unfortunately happened to the Hartley Colliery, drowned for the time being along with six poor men and three boys and five Galloways (pit ponies) and besides the stop to trade.
>
> However, don't be uneasy, the poor people are happy and the water will be got out in a few days. The end to this affair will be a very good one since as soon as the water is off, it will lead them to the fine East seam of coal where they never could approach before for fear of this very body of waste water. I have made a point with your brother that none of the dead bodies when found shall be carried to Hartley, but that their friends (be) sent for to the Pitt, there see them, and so bury them immediately in order to avoid terror among the people as much as possible.

The flood waters must have been pumped away fairly quickly in view of the fact that a second engine put down at Hartley in 1765 appears to have attracted a great deal of attention for it was "drawing coals by fire" at the rate of a corf a minute for some years. It is evident however, that it had its defects, for James Watt, who visited Hartley about 1768, described the engine as going sluggishly and irregularly, having no fly-wheel.

Despite mechanical improvements in water-pumping as well as in coal-raising, the old trouble from the water-feeders continued. This came to a head in 1844 when the workings in the Old Hartley pits were laid in by an inundation of water which was supposed to come from the sea.

In the following year, 1845, operations began on the sinking of a new pit, the Hester Pit. This was the ill-fated disaster pit. The Hester Pit, or the New Hartley Colliery as it was also called, was commenced about a mile and a half to the west of Seaton Delaval Hall and the Low Main Seam was reached, one hundred fathoms down, on 29th May, 1846.

At that time the colliery, the royalty of which belonged to Lord Hastings, was owned by Messrs. Jobling, Carr and Co., but in 1847 the Joblings were bought out by the Carrs, who, about the same time, became the owners of the Cowpen and Burradon collieries in addition to Seghill.

The Hester Pit was unlucky from the start. The Low Main Seam, as it was opened up, was found to be much below the average in thickness. The coal, however, proved better to the east (seawards again!) and the workings were continued in that direction until the same difficulty was encountered which had formerly stopped the colliery. On the 14th February, 1852, with dramatic suddenness torrents of water burst into the mine workings. And, as George Baker Forster tells us in a paper read before the North of England Institute of Mining Engineers on 6th March, 1862 :

> An immense feeder of water came from some pillar workings between the pit and the sea which allowed only a few hours for the drawing of the horses and a portion of the stock.

As a result, the workings were drowned out and the water rose in the shaft to a depth of 420 feet—almost three-quarters of the way up the shaft !

It was obvious to all concerned that the pumping power then in use was utterly inadequate to cope with the great increase of water. A more powerful pumping engine was essential. Hence there was installed at Hartley a pumping engine said to be the most powerful in the north of England. It was a three-hundred horse-power condensing engine with pumps of suitable sizes.

The shaft was 600 feet deep and the water was pumped to bank through pipes in three stages. There was the Low Set of pumps which lifted the water from the sump at the bottom of the shaft to the Yard Seam; then the Middle Set which lifted the water to the High Main Seam; finally the water entered the High Set which raised it up a pumping staple situated alongside the shaft. The power of the engine was such that it was possible to pump to bank 1,500 gallons per minute.

An essential feature of all this pumping machinery was a massive beam made of cast-iron which weighed 42 tons. It was made by the well-known north-country firm of Losh, Wilson and Bell. This beam was anchored in its engine-house close to the top of the shaft and one arm of the beam was poised over the shaft where it see-sawed up and down as it lifted and returned the rods which operated the water-raising gadgets all the way down the shaft.

One morning, with tragic suddenness, this great beam broke in two, one half smashing down the shaft. In his paper given to the mining engineers at Newcastle a few weeks after the disaster, Mr. G. B. Forster described in simple language just what happened :

> On the morning of the accident all was going on as usual; the back-shift men had gone down, and the fore-shift men were still in the pit with the exception of sixteen or seventeen who had ridden and eight of them who were being drawn up in the cage, when, at half-past ten o'clock the outer end of the beam was seen to fall suddenly into the pit.

Like a thunder-bolt the twenty-one tons of cast-iron smashed down the shaft—the only shaft of the pit.

And that was the starting point of one of the greatest mining dramas of all time.

Chapter 3

TRAPPED IN THE PIT-SHAFT

The first act in the tragic drama of Hartley Colliery was that concerning the fate of the cageful of men who were "riding to bank" on that sad Thursday morning.

Eight men were being drawn in the cage up the 600 foot shaft when the disaster occurred. Five of them perished. That three of the men survived to tell the tale was, to say the least, miraculous. When one ponders the affair, the bomb-like crashing down the narrow shaft of a mass of cast-iron twenty-one tons in weight; the resultant smashing of the cage and of the "brattice" and shaft timbers; when one looks at the state of the cage after the crash as revealed by the illustration in this book and reflects that three men emerged alive from that—one must indeed marvel at their fortunate escape.

The names of those killed in the shaft were Robert Bewick, William Brown, Ralph Robson, George Sharp, and his son George Sharp, aged 16 years. The survivors were Ralph Robinson, William Sharp and Thomas Watson.

It is to Thomas Watson, himself, that we are chiefly indebted for a really gripping account of those twelve terrible hours which he spent imprisoned in the shaft. Watson gave evidence at the inquest. Not only that, he was later asked to speak of his experiences at a "devotional meeting" held at a Blackett Street Church, Newcastle upon Tyne, which was reported in the columns of the "Northern Daily Express" for 31st January, 1862. This further resulted in the publication of Watson's experiences in a little book edited on his behalf by a gentleman friend, and published on 11th June, 1862.

To some people this tract of his might be dismissed as a mere pious piece of propaganda. That charge could, perhaps, be levelled against certain of the "sermons" which were preached soon after the disaster and which were subsequently circulated

27

in print. I have perused at least two of these documents which are preserved in the Reference Department of the Newcastle Central Library, and have found them full of moralizings with little regard to material facts about the disaster.

Tom Watson's account is of a different order. He was obviously a man of strong conviction and undoubted integrity. However fanciful and far-fetched one or two of his statements might appear to be (e.g. the strange light which momentarily shone in the shaft) he was, after all, a principal actor in the drama, and his evidence remains an honest man's sincere testimony as to what happened, and must be accepted as such. Having said that, let us share Tom's travail during that memorable day of disaster.

Thomas Watson was a deeply religious man. Religion to him was not just something for observance on Sundays. He gave "witness" in his work at the coal face to the men with whom he came into contact.

Tom was a coal-hewer in the Low Main Seam. He went down the New Hartley Pit at 2-30 a.m. on Thursday, 16th January, 1862, and should, in the normal course of things, have finished his shift at the coal face about 10 a.m.

When, this particular morning, his "back-shift" marrow, George Scurfield came in to relieve him, Tom seemed to be in no hurry to depart. He was somehow pre-occupied in thought. He later told how, during the morning, when Harry Gibson, the putter, came in to change his tub (i.e. to leave an empty tub for Tom's full tub of coal) Harry had said, "What's up this morning, Tom?"

Tom thought for a moment and then replied :

"Ah've just been thinking how nice it will be to walk up to the New Jerusalem after we've got across the Jordan".

"Mebbies we'll not have to walk after we get across—we'll likely be carried".

Such was the significant retort of Harry Gibson, the "hand-putter" as he crouched down to push away the tub of coal from a working-place too low for the use of pit ponies.

Harry Gibson was eighteen years of age. He too was religious, admittedly with a history of devotion less stable than that of Tom Watson's. Some time before this he had been "out of Society", a "back-slider". But only a week before the disaster at a prayer-meeting held in his father's cottage, he had been deeply moved, had shown penitence and had been received back into the fold of the local Society of the Primitive Methodist Connexion. Harry's earlier "fall from Grace" would, in the eyes of his chapel brethren, be abundantly pardoned by his last great act of witness. For we learn from a message left by a disaster victim, James Amour, the back-overman (reproduced elsewhere in this book) that along with Tibbs and others, Harry Gibson fervently prayed and "exhorted" his fellow sufferers as they lay in the Yard Seam awaiting death.

Tom Watson, we have noticed, was in no hurry to go outbye when his marrow George Scurfield came in to relieve him. How little he knew then the value of those few precious minutes ! He finished drilling the hole preparatory to blasting down the coal, and stayed to put in the shot and to fire it.

Eventually, he put on his clothes and came out to the flat where he again met Harry Gibson. Harry's shift did not finish until five o'clock, and this morning Tom did a very unusual thing. He shook hands with Harry—for the last time.

Tom wended his way to the shaft bottom. The cage came down. Tom and others got in making eight in all, four on the upper deck and four on the lower. The onsetter gave the signal on the rapper, and the iron corner chains clanked as they tightened and the cage began to ascend. Then, half way up the shaft something happened.

Tom Watson told the Coroner at the inquest just how it did happen :

> There was a sudden crack and a tremendous crush of stuff . . . timber and stones kept falling about the cage and we made up our minds that the shaft was closed.*

It transpired later that two of the four iron corner chains by which the cage was held had been snapped like threads. Half

---

* Newcastle Courant, 7th February, 1862.

the cage-load of eight men had been cast down the shaft and the other half forced to hang on for dear life to the slanting iron-work of the broken cage.

After the first shock of it all, the survivors tried to find out how things stood. Of course everything was in black darkness, but gradually they became aware of their plight. Ralph Robinson who had been sitting opposite Tom Watson in the cage was now hanging half out of it. William Sharp, brother-in-law of Watson's (as this narrative unfolds it will be seen how closely inter-related families really were in the little community of Hartley)—William Sharp was on the upper deck and was still there, whilst "Old Sharp" was still clinging to the cage but, one of his legs was badly hurt. William Sharp (there had been at the outset three named Sharp, in the cage) somehow got a match from his pocket and struck a light, whilst Tom Watson held a candle to the match—a difficult thing to do whilst holding on to the wrecked cage with the dark abyss below them. The candle-light was, however, quickly extinguished, for water poured down upon them. It must be remembered that the pumps were broken and the water pipes fractured. The men's plight was indeed precarious in the extreme.

"Lord have mercy upon us", cried Old Sharp. And, says Watson, the Lord did have mercy.

In the darkness, Watson groped with one hand around the slimy side of the shaft. He felt one rapper rope, then two, and then a third. And from this fact he gleaned that they were above the Yard Seam, and that it might just be possible for him to climb by means of the ropes to the High Main Seam, if not to the top of the pit. So thinking, he took off his leather belt wherewith to protect his hands, and braced himself for his arduous climb.

But he was stopped ere he started. There was a cry from below, a cry from someone seriously hurt and pleading for help. It was from one of his fellow riders who had been thrown from the cage. Old Sharp recognised the voice as that of his son, and,

30

as Watson said at the inquest, the old man "made a vast of work about the boy" (a telling north-country phrase) and wanted to get down to him but was helpless because of his damaged leg.

"I'll try to get down to him", said Watson, and, so saying, proceeded to slither his way unsteadily down, finding a foothold as best he could on the broken timbers which lined the shaft.

It was a treacherous descent. Black darkness, falling water, jagged projections, from the sides of the shaft, the continual falling of material loosened by the falling of the broken beam, and the inability to get a decent foothold anywhere—all these things made the undertaking difficult in the extreme. Nevertheless, Tom somehow managed to descend about sixty feet chiefly with the guiding aid and support of a slim rapper rope "less thick than a man's little finger".

At last he sensed that he had reached the vicinity of the blockage in the shaft where his work-mates lay amidst the wreckage. Then, whilst holding on with one hand, he reached out with the other towards the place from whence a voice groaned in pain. His hand touched a human head which proved to be that of the boy, George Sharp, who lay half-buried in the tangled ruins. Grasping the boy's shoulder, he tried in vain to pull him clear, but it was no use, for Tom's own foothold was itself none too secure. Nearby, another severely injured man lay groaning, and Tom learned that it was his own brother-in-law, Bob Bewick. Young Sharp's first question was, "Where's me Dad?", and Tom assured him he was quite safe.

There seemed little in these circumstances that human agency could do. So there and then in the darkness, Watson and Sharp prayed to God. Watson, we are told, had been thinking of his cottage home at Old Hartley, where his four motherless children awaited their father's return. He was everything to them, for their mother had died in childbirth five months before. Earnestly Watson and Sharp prayed together. Watson tells us he was not much of a singer but he and Sharp sang a hymn.

What duet was ever sung under such dire circumstances and

under such agonizing extremities ! But in fitful, passionate gasps their hymn ascended the shaft :

> On Jordan's stormy banks I stand
> And cast a wistful eye,
> To Canaan's fair and happy land,
> Where my possessions lie.

Nothing here in this black hole could be more unlike the "Happy Land" of which they had visions, but bravely, if faintly, their soulful duet continued :

> Oh the transporting rapturous scene
> That rises to my sight,
> Sweet fields arrayed in living green,
> And rivers of delight.
>
> All o'er those wide extended plains,
> Shines one eternal day.
> There God the Son forever reigns,
> And scatters night away.

Exhausted by the effort of singing, silence ensued for a while. One can imagine the situation—the occasional fall of stone and rubbish, the constant running, drip-drop sound of water; the low moan of a dying man. Then, prayer once more, but by now the voice of prayer was becoming more faint. Several hours had elapsed since the crash occurred. Bewick and Young Sharp were drawing their last breaths. Tom Watson still clinging to his wire rapper rope, with a slippery foothold on the wet "buntons" was becoming weaker. With his clothes saturated he shivered with cold. Little wonder that more than once he nearly passed out.

Then something happened. Suddenly, the dark, wet shaft became illuminated with a light unearthly. Whether it was a mere figment of imagination on Tom's part, some hallucination induced by the extraordinary situation in which he found himself, he nevertheless swears to the truth of what happened. A great light shone in the shaft. Strange that it should happen just at the moment when Sharp and Bewick were dying, as if, says Watson, it was the passing of the souls from the bodies of the two men. Whatever it was, Watson testified afterwards that it was to him the fact of God's presence in that dark, wet shaft.

THOMAS WATSON

This man was one of three who survived the ordeal of being trapped in the shaft following the wrecking of the cage.

Tom was a man of very fine character, and testified at the Inquest and in other ways, concerning his experiences in the disaster.

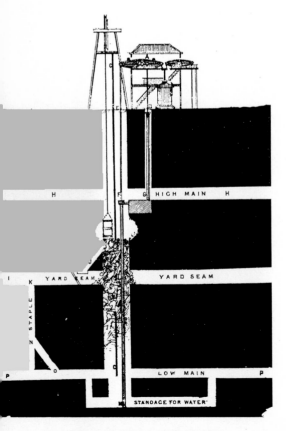

Diagram showing the position of the blockage in the shaft.

THE BLOCKAGE IN THE SHAFT

WILLIAM COULSON

Undoubtedly the most famous pit-sinker of his day, William Coulson had, at the time of the disaster, been 48 years in the work, and had sunk 84 pits, including that of Hartley.

His skilled superintendence of the heroic work at Hartley earned him great praise—and some abuse.

Sinkers about to descend the shaft. The view is from the "Horsehole".

GOING DOWN

It was to him a timely intervention of divine providence. He had come down the pit at 2-30 a.m., it was now about 5 p.m., and it was another six hours before he was rescued. But that flash of kindly light had revealed to him a ledge in the shaft side into which he could crawl away from the constantly falling water and stone, and this doubtless saved his life.

Having rested there for some time he mustered up the courage to try climbing the shaft once more. This time he found and tried the pipes of the pump which ran up the shaft. But his efforts were unavailing and he resigned himself to await any attempts at rescue which might be forthcoming.

Then, after what seemed to be an eternity, help came. The rescuers had come down the staple to the High Main Seam and were now endeavouring to reach them from that point. With all the damage there was no cage in operation, so a "jack rope" was tried. There were sounds of hammering and sawing above them and at last a voice, that of a man named Milburn, called huskily down the shaft, "Hel-lo!"

Someone yelled in answer.

"How many are you?"

"Four", was the reply.

Slowly the darkness of the shaft was dispelled as a rope came down to which a lantern was attached. Old Sharp carefully edged himself into the loop for his badly injured leg was giving him great pain. But he was too fatigued to hold on and another man seized the rope above him and let his legs fall over Sharp's shoulders for protection. He was still insecure, however, and before the High Main Seam was reached, Old Sharp fell out of the loop. He dropped like a stone, bounced off the slanting cage and, with an uncanny thud, struck the debris in the shaft near to where Watson was standing. He died instantly.

After that incident Mr. John Short the engineer in charge of rescue operations at that time, decided to stop using the jack engine for the rescue of the men in the shaft and he instructed his men to use a hand-rope instead.

Billy Sharp was the next to be saved but he nearly didn't manage it for the loop with the lantern went down past him. However, he managed to grasp the rope above the loop and to fasten himself to it by his "neckerchief". The report giving this information says that Billy Sharp "had been a sailor in his early life".

It was now Ralph Robinson's turn, and his rescue appears to have been uneventful.

Finally the rope came down for Watson. Poor Tom's limbs were numb by now, but he got a leg through the loop and grasped the rope. His strength was almost gone. He had scarcely been pulled clear of the bottom than a side of the shaft caved in with a crash followed by a torrent of water. It was a tricky business being hauled up by the toiling rescuers above, despite the fact that they would have a platform across the shaft at the High Main Seam opening—a device mentioned in later rescue operations. As Tom was being hauled up, broken timbers had to be negotiated with great care. And that ugly broken cage with its cruel jagged edges set a problem ! There would be much yelling of "Heave" and "Stop" (or "Hold") and "Lower", before Tom would be got to the High Main Seam. At last he was there. He could battle no longer. He collapsed in a faint in the arms of his rescuers. Cold, fatigued, the whole protracted ordeal of exposure and strain proved too much for the biggest-hearted and bravest of men. After all it was now about 11 p.m., twelve hours after the cage had been "rapped to bank" on its fateful journey. Tom was put into bed in a colliery house near the pit, and carefully tended. When he regained consciousness, his father, who had been sent for, sat by his bedside.

Slowly, recognition dawned. Out of the mists of unconsciousness Tom's mind wandered back to the nightmare of his recent experiences when trapped in the shaft. He pondered over the fact of his survival, a miraculous deliverance which he attributed to the mercy of God.

Then turning his face to his father, he said feelingly :
"Oh, father, what a blessed thing religion is!"

And as if his father was unaware of the blessings of religious experience and the glad tidings of the Gospel, Tom added :

"Now is the time to try it".

So saying, he lifted his eyes to the ceiling. A smile played about the lips of his drawn face, as if the plain whitewash of the ceiling enshrined for him secret visions of Heaven beheld through vistas of angels. His lips moved once more in prayer, this time in a prayer of thanksgiving, his knowledge of the scriptures recollecting a passage appropriate to the present occasion :

> He brought me up also out of an horrible pit, out of the miry clay and set my feet upon a rock. And He hath put a new song in my mouth, even praise unto our God.

PART TWO

The Heroic Struggle of the Sinkers

Chapter 1

OPERATION RESCUE

The great task of rescue was begun with all possible speed. It was started with that sense of urgency which the situation demanded, but it was an extremely difficult undertaking, and one fraught with great danger.

At the outset the operation was in the hands of Mr. John Short, enginewright of the colliery. He it was who brought out the men who were trapped in the shaft and who got to bank the cages, one of which was so badly battered.

But on the day after the disaster a man arrived from Durham who offered his services in the great work which lay ahead. He was no stranger here. He was without doubt the best qualified person living for such a task and he was at once put in charge of the whole operation. His name was Coulson.

William Coulson was known throughout the North of England. He was now getting on in years, but in his knowledge and experience of pit-sinking, he was without equal. It is perhaps just as well at this stage to say a few words concerning his credentials because, during the rescue work, protracted as it unavoidably was, there were angry mutterings of discontent on the part of a small minority at Hartley whose feelings got vent by outbursts of abuse directed at Coulson. "Shoot Coulson!" cried a fanatical few in angry desperation at the delay in getting at the entombed men.

But Coulson's position was really unassailable. At the inquest, Mr. Kenyon Blackwell, an Inspector of Mines from the Midlands, who attended the inquest by order of the Home Secretary, brought out a few facts about Coulson's unique experience as the following extract shows :

BLACKWELL : You have had a great experience in sinking, more so, I believe than any other man in the country ?

COULSON : Yes, I think I have had a longer experience and more of it. I have been about 48 years a sinker.

BLACKWELL : Did you sink this shaft ?

COULSON : I did.

BLACKWELL : How many years ago ?

COULSON : Seventeen.

Coulson went on to say that he had sunk in all about 84 pit shafts, a truly remarkable performance.

Naturally Coulson, after so many years in this work, had gathered around him his own gang of men, all expert sinkers whom he brought to Hartley with him. There was Billy Coulson, his son, Geordie Emmerson, Billy Shields, Davy Wilkinson and several others. These men, along with the colliery "viewers" and practical pitmen from adjacent collieries, made a competent team with rare qualities of skill, daring, endurance and resource.

Those were the rescuers. What of their task ? When we analyse the situation which they found at the pit, the whole position appeared to be utterly hopeless.

Perhaps we could approach the rescuers' problem by asking a single pertinent question : How did it come about that a disaster of this magnitude could happen at Hartley ? Without anticipating the arguments and conclusions to which the disaster gave rise, it seems necessary from the start to point to a few factors which affected the whole position.

In the extraordinary combination of circumstances which caused the loss of so many lives, the first consideration of importance is **The Fact of the Single Shaft.** That all those men could be working six hundred feet below the ground with nothing between them and safety but one shaft 12 feet 6 inches in diameter, which served at once as inlet and outlet for the men, which received down one half, the fresh air from the surface and returned up the other the foul air from the pit, a shaft which was cluttered with cages and ropes and buntons and water-pipes; that such a thing should obtain seems to have been an incredible and intolerable state of affairs. More is said in a later chapter concerning this particular aspect, but suffice it to say here that this disastrous experience, tragic as it was, fortunately led to legislation being enacted which stipulated thereafter the provision of two shafts or outlets to every pit.

A second factor was **The Timing of the Disaster.** We have already seen that a shift of men had just descended the pit in order to relieve their "fore-shift marrows". In other words a fresh batch of men was proceeding to take the place of those who had gone to work several hours earlier, and the disaster occurred just at the very time when both sets of men were underground together.

A third important consideration was **The Place of the Stoppage in the Shaft.** Some idea of the different seams at the colliery has already been given. First in going down the shaft was the High Main, then the Yard Seam, and then the Low Main Seam. Only the last-named was being worked, and it was in that seam, the Low Main, where the men were when the disaster occurred.

It was indeed a cruel twist of fate which caused the stoppage to happen just where it did. To illustrate this more clearly let us divide the shaft into three horizontal sections. Had the stoppage occurred in the top third, all well and good, the men would have escaped up the water-pumping staple which had been sunk alongside the shaft; had it happened in the bottom third, they could, as indeed they did, escape up the staple connecting the Low Main with the Yard Seam; but the vital weakness was in the middle section—**there was no inter-communication between the Yard and High Main Seams.** And since that is precisely where the stoppage of the shaft occurred, where all the wreckage accumulated, the fate of the men below was more or less sealed from the start.

Arising from the fact of the blockage happening where it did in this single shaft, a fourth factor becomes evident. That was **The Paralysis of the Pit's System of Ventilation.** The method of ventilation was for the shaft to be divided down the middle by a wooden partition or "brattice". Down one side of this the fresh air descended to circulate around the workings of the pit from whence it returned to the surface via the other side of the partition in the shaft. One side of the partition was called the

41

"downcast" and the other side, the "upcast". Near the base of the upcast, a furnace fire was kept burning which was the chief agent in that system of ventilation. In effect the upcast shaft was a very big chimney up which the smoke, heat and foul air escaped or were pulled from the pit.

It naturally follows that once the partition between these two air passages was smashed and the shaft blocked, the men were not only prisoners in a tomb, but also bereft of fresh air from the surface, for the smouldering furnace fire used up the little air left in the pit. So it was that the pit became foul with gas, and the men died in a manner summed up by the Coroner at the inquest, "from the inhalation of gas, being shut up in the Yard Seam of the said colliery".

It will be seen that the task facing the rescue team was one not only difficult and dangerous, but almost certainly foredoomed to failure. But those brave men pushed on regardless of the peril below and the measure of abuse that was meted out to them from above. For they were stout of heart, with a pride in their calling and a genuine love of their fellow men. So despite the odds against them they battled on, inspired by that hope which springs eternal in the human breast.

Chapter 2

MR. FORSTER'S NARRATIVE

As indicated in the previous chapter, the first persons to enter the shaft after the breaking of the beam, were Mr. Short, egine-wright of the colliery, and a few of his workmen. Since there was no cage in which they could travel, their only means of getting down the pit was by the jack-engine and the crab-rope, which meant, in the main, travelling in a sling at the end of a rope.

They found the shaft a complete wreck. The brattice was destroyed, the cage slides and buntons knocked out or damaged, and the main "dry spears" or pump rods broken for some distance from the surface. As all the timbers were hanging in a very dangerous state, their progress downward was indeed very slow.

In the meantime another party of men went down the pumping staple in order to tackle, from below, the wreckage which had accumulated at the first level, that of the High Main Seam. These men succeeded so far that by the afternoon of the day of the disaster (Thursday) they were able to get the jack-rope through the wreckage above by means of a hand-line. They then got into communication with the men in the shaft below, and, as we have seen, proceeded to lower a light to them and to effect their rescue. It will be remembered that this jack-rope was used in the attempt to haul up Old Sharp, but, as one account tells us : "in coming away, he unfortunately got fast, was pulled out of the loop, and, falling on the wreck below, was killed".

At this stage a consultation of pit officials was held and it was deemed advisable to put in a temporary scaffold or platform across the shaft at the level of the High Main Seam. The reason for this was to prevent the timber, etc., which fell from the men working above, from going down the shaft to increase the

43

danger and the difficulties of those working below. The work of clearing the shaft was then resumed and in a few hours all the timbers which had been left hanging in a dangerous state above the High Main were either taken out to the surface or thrown down to the scaffold, from whence men took them into some nearby drifts and "stow-bords" of the High Main Seam. Before morning the two cages were got out of the shaft, one of which was in a very battered condition.

Mr. G. B. Forster, mining engineer, was in close touch with the Hartley rescue operation, and his paper, given to the North of England Institute of Mining Engineers a few weeks after the disaster, summarises the day-to-day progress of the work. His account is factual and includes diagrams and statistics. In order that the reader might get a compact picture of the labours of the sinkers during that ill-fated week, I propose in the present chapter, to refer to Mr. Forster's day-to-day account of how the work went on, and to reserve for subsequent chapters the fuller and more deeply human story which Mr. T. Wemyss Reid has to tell, reporting as he does the feelings and emotions of the people at the pit-head, and giving evidence in his chronicle of sympathetic insight into the facts of the Hartley scene.

Thursday, 16th January—Disaster Day. The initial work has already been referred to. That was the rescue of those trapped in the shaft, the removal of the cages, and the clearance of some of the wreckage.

Friday, 17th—The work was pushed on and a point was reached about 100 feet below the High Main Seam. It was then found that the obstruction had assumed a very consolidated form, timbers were jammed together in hopeless confusion and inevitably the work now proceeded very slowly. Mr. W. Coulson, master sinker, arrived at Hartley and his expert services were readily accepted.

Saturday, 18th—The work continued with "tolerable success". Much of the smashed timber had been reduced to matchwood and had to be filled into the corves with shovels. During the day the sides of the shaft began to give way and a quantity of stone fell from time to time. Towards evening this got worse and it was necessary to stop the work of sinking until new timber supports were put around the sides of the shaft. This was done, not only for safety, but to facilitate the work in general. The task occupied about twelve very precious hours.

Sunday, 19th—The timbering having been completed, work on clearing the wreckage was resumed. It was estimated that the rescuers were only 30 feet from the Yard Seam and the entombed men. Coulson decided to concentrate the work on that side of the shaft where the pipes of the pumping apparatus were situated in the hope that it would be possible to make a hole down the side of the pipes. But the timbers were found to be wedged tightly about the pipes, and each time the crab-rope hauled out a length of timber, small stone and rubbish rushed down to fill the space that was left.

Monday, 20th — Great hopes were entertained that on reaching "the bucket door scaffold" (a part of the pumping system where there was a small side-platform for supporting and servicing the pumps) that it would be found whole, and that there would be a hollow space underneath it, near the mouth of the furnace drift, leading to the Yard Seam. On this day the sinkers, after "the most strenuous efforts" reached this point. But there was evidence now of a new danger which filled these anxious men full of foreboding. That was gas.

Up to the present no serious apprehensions had been felt about the fate of the entombed men except that concerning their want of food and rest. Nearly everyone in the pit knew of that staple way of escape from the Low Main to the Yard Seam, and the pit officials had instructions as to its use in any emergency. Hence it was rightly assumed that the men, led by Jim Amour, the back-overman, would have come up that way to the Yard Seam, which is, in fact, what they did. Moreover, "jowling" signals had been heard on Friday which appeared to come from near the shaft at the Yard Seam level.

But now a new dread cast down the spirits of those concerned in the work of rescue. Let me now quote Mr. Forster's own words :

45

On Monday a new enemy began to develop. A vapour had been observed coming out of the pumps . . . During the night the sinkers, at each change of shift, began to show symptoms of sickness and nausea on coming into the fresh air, and it became evident that they were under the influence of some gas which produced these effects. It was at first thought to be "stythe" or carbonic acid gas; the fact, however, of the lights not being subdued by it, but on the contrary burning freely, and if anything with increased flame, led us to suppose it must be carbonic oxide.

It may be of interest here to remark that Coulson stated at the inquest that his men working in the shaft were using common candles for illumination, and that the effect of the gas was to make the flames burn brighter.

Tuesday, 21st—Early this morning the sinkers reached the pump scaffold already mentioned. Then something happened which confirmed the fears already held about the gas. On pulling out from the tangled wreckage a piece of timber rather larger than usual "the gas came away in immense volumes", overpowering the men in the bottom to such an extent that it was with the greatest difficulty they escaped. Even the men in the High Main Seam were severely affected by it and were brought to bank extremely ill.

There was now only one course of action open to Coulson. Work on further clearance must stop. Dreadful as this news must be to the waiting relatives of the entombed men, it would be fatal to go on unless the ventilation was restored. Despite the fact that the rescuers were so near to the furnace drift entrance to the Yard Seam, this gas had to be cleared away before another attempt was made to push on with the sinking.

Preparations were therefore made to that end. In place of the smashed wooden partition which had previously divided the shaft into two airways, there was now to be installed a temporary partition made of brattice-cloth fastened to the battens. A sufficient stock of bales of brattice-cloth not being available at Hartley, a supply was obtained from Seaham Colliery. All this meant a delay of at least 24 hours.

Then it was no easy matter fixing the brattice cloth in the shaft because it was necessary to wrap around, and enclose, the water pipes and pumps. But it was done eventually and this rather complicated system of ventilation went into action. It consisted of the "downcast" side of the cloth brattice with its current of fresh air, assisted in its course down the shaft by an artificial water-fall. On the "upcast" side of the brattice the foul air and gas were taken to the High Main Seam, and from thence up the staple to the boiler fires of the engine house at the top of the pit, where the engine house chimney was utilised to exercise its pull on the return air current.

Wednesday, 22nd—This morning the brattice was completed and the sinkers resumed their work of clearing away the rubbish at the stoppage in the shaft. About mid-day a small hole was made through the obstruction and the men reached the entrance to the furnace-drift leading to the Yard Seam. But the gas was now so strong that they dare not enter the drift. Eventually the gas cleared somewhat, and one or two of the sinkers squeezed through a hole just large enough for a man to edge his way in. They advanced cautiously into the drift where they came across workmen's tools. Two axes were found, and a saw and a "back-skin", and there was evidence to show that the men had been trying to clear a way out from the drift at the approach to the shaft. Then they found bodies, two of them near the furnace. As they advanced they saw more and more bodies . . .

Having ascertained that there was now no life to be saved, and in view of the fact that the roadways, as well as the shaft, were in a treacherous condition, and above all that there was still a considerable amount of gas in the seam which repeatedly forced the men to withdraw, it was decided to repair the roadways and improve the ventilation at once, before risking any further the lives of the rescuers.

Thursday, 23rd—The above-mentioned work occupied the whole of today.

Friday, 24th—Nothing now remained to be done but to clear away the last of the rubbish and to complete the brattice into the Yard Seam. To quote Forster's own words: "The gas and stench were at times so strong as almost to prevent the men from working in the pit".

Saturday, 25th—By ten o'clock this morning everything was now ready for sending the bodies to bank. As some of the bodies were considerably decomposed it was deemed necessary by the medical men to have a good supply of chloride of lime, and everyone who went down to assist in removing them was provided with a strong pair of leather gloves.

It had originally been arranged to send the coffins down the pit, but eventually the dead were sent up out of the pit in sling chains and coffined at the surface. This materially facilitated the task as it would have occupied a considerable time to coffin the bodies in the pit. Moreover, the position of the pumps, etc., in the shaft would have made it difficult to bring the coffins safely past them. Thus the sinkers, after the most heroic and sustained efforts, had at last opened the way to the recovery of the bodies.

At half-past ten today (Saturday) the first body was brought to bank. Parties of men from neighbouring collieries were told off to relieve each other in the labour of bringing the corpses from where they were lying in the pit to the vicinity of the shaft in the Yard Seam. Each body was then fastened in a sling and hoisted to the surface. A "rider" went up on each journey. That is to say a sinker accompanied each body up the shaft. He was slung in a loop just above the dead man and it was his job to guide the body to the surface so as to prevent it being dashed against the side of the shaft.

This dreadful work went on without intermission for seventeen and a half hours until four o'clock on the Sunday morning, when it was announced that all the bodies found in the vicinity of the shaft, 199 in number, had been brought to bank.

Some speculation then arose as to how many men there really were down the pit at the time the disaster happened. Hence a search was made. The search party set out, greatly daring because of the gas in the pit, to explore every part of the Yard Seam and the Low Main. With the greatest difficulty they

VIGIL BY NIGHT

A group of relatives of the entombed men waiting at the pit-head.

"WAITING OF THE NEWS"

This illustration is one of a pair of Hartley pictures given to the author by Miss
E. Garrigan of Seaham. They had been hung in the family home for generations.

The above picture is reproduced with caption as per the original print. The
artist has obviously captured something of the sombre reality of the scene at t!
pit-head, with sinkers awaiting their turn to descend the pit, and relatives of
entombed men suffering all the agonies of suspense in their long wait for r

THE HASTINGS ARMS

In certain press reports of 1862 the Hastings Arms is mentioned as "the only Inn within a couple of miles". It was described as "literally swarming" with the many visitors who came to the scene of the disaster.

PHOTO (1962) BY J. E. McCUTCHEON.

BRINGING UP THE BODIES

the disaster occurred, there began the grim task of raising the bodies
m the Hartley Pit. The work went on non-stop for 17½ hours. Each
g at the end of a rope and hauled up the shaft. A sinker rode just above
prevent it being dashed against the shaft sides. On the left are a few of
Note the protective headgear of the sinkers.

PHOTO-COPY BY J. C. CURRY

penetrated every part of the Yard Seam. They next reached the point at the staple where the Yard Seam communicated with the Low Main. There they were halted. When so far down they discovered the staple had eight or ten feet of water in the bottom which meant that the Low Main Seam was flooded, as indeed was to be expected since the beam of the pumping engine was broken. This, concludes Mr. Forster, of course put an end to any further search :

And it was ascertained by a careful computation, that the 199 found in the Yard Seam, with the five who were killed in the shaft making 204 in all, were the whole of those lost by this most terrible catastrophe.

Chapter 3

HOPE SPRINGS ETERNAL

In his perusal of the last few pages the reader must surely have identified himself with the battle which the sinkers waged in the Hartley shaft. The most unimaginative person must have gone down that abyss dangling on the end of a rope with each sinker; he must have toiled and sweated, been soaked with water, bruised by falling materials, and become ill with gas; he must have experienced the frustration occasioned by outrageous fortune in this struggle for victory. As our story unfolds he will doubtless feel a mighty sense of relief to see the sinker win through even if it is merely to recover dead bodies from the jaws of the pit and to see them restored to their loved ones for respectful interment.

But what, in the meantime, of the scene "at bank", at the top of the pit. The narrative of T. Wemyss Reid gives the answer. He describes the tragedy enacted there with its heartbreak at the heart of things.

The paramount impression one gets from his account is that of the prolonged agony of suspense. People waited. They waited and hoped. Time dragged on with leaden feet as it did with the prisoner in "The Ballad of Reading Gaol", when

. . . Each day is like a year. A year whose days are long.

The waiters hoped against hope until hope was finally crushed by the last enemy of Death. It was indeed a cruel consummation to the prolonged agony of suspense to see one's loved one hauled from the pit, a stiffened and slimy corpse, swinging and rotating repulsively at the end of a rope.

T. Wemyss Reid sets the scene for us. This place, he says, is now a centre of the deepest interest to all the inhabitants of the British Isles. The pit is situated close to the Blyth and Tyne Railway and within a stone's throw of Hartley Station. All the buildings are surrounded by, and indeed appear to be erected upon, a huge pit-heap composed of stone and other material wrought in the mine. The first objects which attract the attention of the visitor as he climbs up this heap are the gins which are lifting the material gathered by the sinkers in the shaft. Around these at all times stand a number of men ready to assist in turning the machines. He points out that as the work is continually going on, it is a great strain on the horses which go round and round with the gin. There are three small engines in use, the gin, the jack and the crab. Not far away are the boilers of the now useless pumping engines, and at the other side of the heap are the joiners' and smiths' shops.

But the centre piece of all is the raised pit-heap platform near the shaft opening. Here are gathered together the important people of this and the neighbouring collieries. Police Superintendent Wookey is there, also the local doctors, the clergy, the press-men, etc.

Below this platform stand the relatives of the entombed men waiting and watching. They eagerly follow each movement of the jack engine rope as it raises something, anything, from the deep. They listen to any whisper of knowledge which might be forthcoming as to what is happening up there on the platform. Around and about these relatives, multitudes of visitors and sightseers constantly crowd in, arriving by train, by horse or donkey-drawn cart, and on foot. There are fellow-miners from all over the northern coalfield, many of whom are there to offer help in rescue work. Others, more militant, and, with increasing fervour as time goes on, voice their disgust and indignation that such a thing should have been allowed to happen to their comrades of the deep.

Out of the centre of this mass of humanity, pit-heaps and pulley-wheels rise up to heaven, the cynosure of all eyes, like some strange altar to an unknown god.

Mr. Reid lists the various prominent people who keep coming and going as the rescue work proceeds. Here are a few of the names : Mr. Fryer, viewer, Teams Colliery, Newcastle;

Mr. Sanderson, viewer, and Mr. Marshall, engineer, of Seaton Delaval Colliery; Mr. Potter, owner and viewer of Cramlington Colliery; Mr. Crone, West Moor Colliery; Mr. Hurst, Backworth; Mr. Ramsay, Walbottle; Mr. G. B. Forster, Cowpen; Mr. T. E. Forster, Seaton Delaval; Mr. Maddison, Burradon; Mr. Jobling, Bebside; Mr. Middleton, Bedlington; Mr. Matthias Dunn, Government Inspector of Mines; Mr. Nicholas Wood, President of the Institute of Mining Engineers; Mr. James Mather, South Shields; Mr. Hugh Taylor, Chairman of the Coal Trade, and many others. Mr. Carr, viewer, and Mr. Humble, under-viewer, were in constant attendance as the chief representatives of the local owners and managers. Now and again a conference took place of all the viewers on the spot, and for this purpose they adjourned to a miner's cottage nearby.

We are told that "a hundred suggestions" were made by people scattered all over the country as to how best to get at the men in the pit. For example, a telegram was received from a Mr. Hill of Bristol advising the rescuers to bore a small hole down the shaft through the rubbish and by this means pour down soup to the men below. Another idea was to remove the buckets from the pumps and then to force provisions down the pipe. Mr. Forster said fortunately this was not tried as it was later found that the pumps were completely jammed by broken wood, etc. Perhaps the most preposterous of the suggestions made was to get the other half of the broken beam on its end (21 tons of it) and to drop it down the shaft "in the hope that its ponderous body falling upon the obstruction would clear it entirely away". This plan was rejected as being too dangerous to be attempted. Finally, we are told, after much anxious consultation, the united opinion of the most eminent viewers of the day was that Mr. Coulson's was the only practical plan, and that this must be followed with the utmost possible vigour.

There was no lack of volunteers for the job. These were "signed on" by Mr. Emmerson the able assistant of Mr. Coulson. Mr. Reid was present at the pit-heap when a gang of nine men arrived from a colliery at a considerable distance. "You sent for three", they said, "but we thought you might want more".

This, Reid adds, shows the spirit obtaining there as men arrived from north, south and west.

Picture after picture is given by Mr. Reid of the scene at the pit-head and I incorporate a few of his word-pictures in the following paragraphs.

When the day broke this (Saturday) morning a mournful and impressive scene was presented at the mouth of the pit. Two huge fires burning near the shaft cast a sickly flame of light upon the tall engine-house, and the cage which was broken on Thursday was now lying a battered mass of metal upon the heap. Occasionally the hoarse cries of the men at the engines as they gave the signals received from below, rang through the keen frosty air, and the gin, the jack and the crab, as the case might be, moved responsive to the order.

Every two hours a relay of men, picked as crack hands from the collieries in the neighbourhood, are lowered one by one, perilously and slowly, down the black pit by means of a heavy chain. Two of them are suspended by ropes, in order not to touch the rubbish which might fall at any moment and they go down as far as possible, and then, as quickly and as gently as they can, they clear away the obstruction, placing it in a "corf" which is at once received by their comrades stationed at intervals above them, and, being passed quickly upwards, is shot into the top seam, which is as yet clear.

Around the pit buildings a crowd of men is gathered, they talk to each other in undertones, speculating upon the fate of their comrades. Whenever the gin needs to be turned they volunteer for the service, for the horses are thoroughly worn out with the labour through which they have gone. At other times they stand idly and silently, apparently quite unconscious of the bitter blast which is sweeping in from the sea with chilling force. Occasionally one or two women with tearless faces, paralysed with "the hope deferred that maketh the heart sick" come from the village to know if anything has transpired regarding the fate of their loved ones, and then, with fixed, stony countenances the sight of which is far more moving than any violent outbursts of passion would be, slowly return to their desolate homes.

It is bitterly cold and a few flakes of snow are falling, but our patient group of watchers is still gathered around one of the huge fires waiting. In a rude cabin close at hand are collected the men who are engaged on the different shifts of work, each quietly awaiting his particular turn. Once in two hours a party of strange looking objects enveloped in huge "back-skins" made of leather, and heavy helmets made of similar material, are hauled up to the surface, and these, making their way to the cabin, change their wet clothes, while their places below are taken by others. Whatever may be the tone of feeling amongst casual visitors in regard to this great calamity, these noble-hearted men, who are ready to lay down their lives for their brother workmen, brothers whom many of them have never seen in the flesh, look upon it with all the solemnity which such an event demands.

When a man comes in from his shift, he is eagerly questioned as to the progress that has been made, and his statement of the nature of the work is listened to with the intensest interest. Now and then a pleasing recognition takes place between old comrades who, long separated, have been brought to the same spot by a common motive of charity. All, however, is quiet and nothing incongruous with the painful nature of the circumstances goes on. Accidents like this call forth the noblest qualities of the Northumbrian miner. Some incidents indeed, have transpired, which belong to the heroic, and are deserving of being recorded in letters of gold.

The next paragraph was written by Mr. Reid at 5 a.m. on the Sunday following the disaster :

All around the pit-heap the watch-fires are still burning, and the patient waiters, looking more solemn and despairing than ever are clustered near them. They have withstood the severity of one of the bitterest nights we have had during the present winter, and as yet they show no signs of giving in. Now and then there emerges from the gloom the figure of a female, who, after another sleepless night, has come forth to learn the news. Her face, as she hears how little has been done to save those whom she so tenderly loves, assumes an aspect which can never be forgotten by those who have once seen it.

One thing however is noticeable with regard to the women. Whenever they come amongst the workers or the waiters they are treated with a silent and respectful sympathy which speaks volumes for those who tender it. These men rugged, uncouth and wayward in their dispositions as they generally are, have become for the moment knights-gallant, as gentle and as courteous as the stainless Bayard himself. In the rude cabin to which I have so often alluded, a scene worthy of the genius of Salvator Rosa may be witnessed. A blazing fire is casting a vivid light upon the toil-stained men who surround it, clad as they are in the strangest and most unpromising garments, and whose countenances are tell-tale indexes to the thoughts that fill their minds. They have been waiting for their own shift all the night through and are still as patient as ever.

The discerning eye of Mr. Reid continues to observe, and he records with feeling and sincerity what he sees   .   .   .

The waiting relatives, he says, cluster in anxious groups. It would rend a heart of stone to see the longing eyes with which they follow every man as he disappears down the shaft, and the breathless interest with which they watch the coming back of the shift to learn the varying success with which they have met.

Passing from this painful spot we may scramble up a heap of coals to the iron platform at the head of the shaft. Here a curious sight is presented. In the background is the yawning chasm, black and dangerous looking, down which the mighty beam fell with irresistible force. Huge timbers torn and twisted like pieces of paper, evidence, in a small degree, of the violence and the frightful velocity with which the fatal mass of metal dropped through the air.

Standing here, beside the huge fires which cast a brilliant light upon the scene are the superintendents at "bank" as the place is called. These are Mr. Humble, the resident viewer, who has hardly known what sleep is since the fatal occurrence, and now and then Mr. Forster, jnr., Mr. Carr and Mr. Taylor. Close by Mr. Humble, listening at the mouth of the pit-shaft are the two signal-men. Occasionally a totally unintelligible shout comes up from the workers below, the lights of whose candles may be dimly seen far away down. But these signals are instantly interpreted and repeated by the signal-men who cry out in strange, hoarse tones, "Bend up the jack" or "Lower the gin" or "Heave up the crab", as the case may be. Then a rumbling sound is heard and one of the three ropes passing down the shaft moves slowly in obedience to the call. Upon the correctness of these signal-men the lives of all the workers below, and consequently, of the prisoners too, constantly depends. A single false word would be more fatal here than in the case of a ship flying close past a rock-bound coast.

Just behind the shaft is the lofty engine-house. Entering this and climbing up the staircase past a perfect labyrinth of machinery, we come at last to the remaining portion of the broken beam. The whole beam was of the enormous weight of forty-two tons, and that portion now lying somewhere or other in the shaft weighs twenty-one tons. By a little exertion we obtain a perfect view of the iron at that point where it was broken off . . .

      *   *   *

Throughout this chronicle of Reid's there is one word which keeps recurring. It is the word hope. For hope springs eternal in the human breast. It is the silver lining to this black cloud of tragedy at Hartley.

On the very first day he says, "A few hours will decide the issue". A little later he assures us hopefully that "at any moment the obstruction may give way with a run" and the prisoners will be rescued. When he leaves the pit-heap for a short while to walk down the village street he gazes through the windows of the miners' cottages and he sees evidence of hope in the fact that each table is set with the breakfast things prepared for the husband who may return at any moment, even if "the face of the woman, seen above the window-blind, is marked by the same cold agony that distinguishes all".

On the Saturday after the disaster he says, "hopes are entertained that during the night an end will be put to all suspense", and later that same day he gives utterance to a cry, "Hope at last, thank God!" Hope is sustained by the hearing of "jowling" signals given by the men entombed; hope is evident in Dr. Davison's preparation of stretchers, hot tea, brandy, blankets, etc. Moreover, in every cottage beds are ready, and at the school-house there is a large supply of tea, soup, jelly, preserved beef, etc., for the men who will surely return. Hope is further buoyed up by the fact discussed freely by the men at bank who say there's always the oats in the pony-stables below ground for the men to feed upon, and, at the very worst there's the pit ponies themselves which might be cut up to feed starving men.

Admittedly, there would be a difficulty with regard to the ponies. There were no less than 43 ponies working in the Low Main and it would be impossible to get them up the staple from the Low Main to the Yard Seam along with the men. So they would be left to run wild in panic and terror until they were mercifully engulfed by the rising flood-waters consequent upon the breakdown of the pumping engine. Nevertheless there were one or two ponies at the Yard Seam level and these might be sacrificed in the dire emergency referred to above.

Such were the speculations upon which hope sought increasingly to lean for assurance. Sometimes the rescuers seemed so near to the journey's end only to be thrust back once again to where they were before. On the Monday afternoon, Mr. Reid quotes the authority of Mr. Coulson for saying that he hopes to reach the men in four hours time. But at the expiration of the four hours Reid has to say, "Again we have to record the falsification of fondly cherished hopes". It is the old story. The fire of hope had burned brightly, the eager anticipations had been aroused, only to be damped down once more. So they had to settle down once again to the work of watching and waiting.

Thus did day follow day with oppressive slowness during that memorable week. And so the long drawn-out vigil, so full of hope for the most part, reached its final dramatic climax. A grim battle for life and death is going on here, Reid says, but the fearful tragedy is being played out. The flame of hope is almost extinguished when he remarks, "We are patiently awaiting the result which we scarcely know whether to dread or to hope for". Then hope is finally abandoned when he pens the following lines :

> The very heart sickens and the hand palsies as I write these lines and anticipate a dreadful conclusion to our long and painful watch.

Reid knew that the battle was over.

Chapter 4

MASS MEETINGS OF PROTEST AT THE PIT

The various chroniclers of the Hartley story in the Press and elsewhere describe at some length the many mass meetings which took place in the grim setting around the pit-heap during that fateful week.

There were on the one hand, as we shall see later, the meetings called for prayer and devotion. And on the other hand the mass meetings of protest, protest at the lack of information given by those in authority; protest at the slowness of the rescue work, and so on. Later on there was to be evidence, in the great meetings held in Newcastle, of an organised body of protest at the shortcomings of the existing mining law and practice (e.g. the single shaft) with a passionate advocacy of the case for legislation on the matter.

Meanwhile, here at Hartley, the situation was full of emotion and drama. Against this background of the pit-buildings and pulley-wheels, the grim realities of it all impressed reporters whose job it was to tell the world, and the result was a vivid record of the happenings there.

Reid describes to us the build up of the great crowd which assembled on that first Sunday after the disaster occurred. It appears that from then on the scene took on a different character, or at least a new element attached itself to the local folk gathered around the pit. There has always been that section of the population which could turn a situation, however grave, into a mere spectacular diversion. So Hartley became to some people a sort of circus to be indulged in with heartless and indecent gaiety.

The neighbourhood of the pit-head, says Reid, now wears a different aspect. An immense crowd is gathered all around the base of the mound on which the pit buildings stand, and the people are watching the working of the engines, and chatting and talking as if it were some curious spectacle they were witnessing. All along the Blyth and Tyne Railway which passes within a dozen yards of where we stand, he says, an unceasing crowd of people is streaming towards the colliery. Men, women and children have come from all parts of the country to gratify their morbid curiosity. The trains have brought vast bodies of visitors from Newcastle, Blyth and Shields, and it is computed that not less than 20,000 persons have visited the scene of the calamity during the day. "The Hastings Arms", the only inn within a couple of miles, is literally swarming with visitors, passages and staircases being alike impassable, and, with a callousness that is positively shocking, all are drinking, joking and enjoying themselves as if they were out upon some holiday. The scene is altogether a striking one, and we trust it may be long ere another such Sabbath desecrates this district.

Then, Reid, in a masterly manner, switches his spotlight away from the merry-makers in the pub, back to the scene at the pit where, with a very different aspect, the watchers are still waiting for the release of those whom they love. "They are gathered together by themselves and their feelings must be deeply wounded by the heartlessness displayed by the strangers around them".

In view of the great crowds which now and then pressed towards the shaft, it was deemed necessary to get the colliery joiners to erect barriers to keep them back from the pit-head where the banksmen were receiving their signals from below, and other exacting work was being carried on. But it took more than a mere barrier fence to keep some of them back. Reid tells us that the outsiders who swarmed about the place were kept from the pit by a body of the County Police "under the active and intelligent supervision of Mr. Superintendent Wookey".

Of course it was not just idle curiosity on the part of many in the great crowd. There were those like "the man from the Potteries in Staffordshire" who once lived at Hartley and had a lot of friends and relations there. After an absence of 16 years

60

he had travelled back all one night to his native place to try to ascertain what had befallen his people".

Reid again swings his camera over the multitude to fasten this time upon one dejected face amongst those who waited. This was "the poor creature named Smith" whose son and grandson were down the pit at the time of the accident and who had sat at the pit, pensive and silent, immovable as a stone, ever since it happened. Smith's interest was momentarily awakened in the dark hours of the night (it was one a.m. on Monday morning to be precise) when there was a great commotion in the crowd and it was at first thought that some of the entombed men were being rescued. But it was merely the bringing to bank of the bodies of the five men who were killed in the shaft on Thursday, and who had, in the meantime, lain in a temporary resting place in the High Main Seam.

It was about this time, late Monday or early Tuesday, that a feeling of exasperation began to show itself. The patience of many, even the long-suffering locals, had been sorely tried, and it was now almost exhausted. "What are they doing?" they cried, "Why doesn't somebody tell us what is happening?" and so on.

The excitement grew. Men murmured one to another. They raised their voices. They gesticulated. They shouted abuse, and finally some of them forced their way past the police, mounted the platform in a menacing manner, demanded to be told just what was going on and why the men, or the bodies, were not being got out of the pit.

Dr. Thomas Hodgkin, in an account written at the time of the disaster tells us :

On Tuesday when the group around the pit began to grow uneasy and turbulent, suspecting that all was not being done that might be done for the rescue of their comrades, Coulson made a little harangue to them, at the end of which he said "There is no danger for the men, unless there be stythe in the pit, but to tell you the truth I am afraid there is stythe". Slowly these fears darkened.

We can imagine the tense look on the sea of faces staring up eagerly, in the light of the brazier fires, as the care-worn

61

master-sinker stood before them, clad in his protective shaft-clothing of "back-skin", and leather hat with its neck-curtain attached, all of which were glistening and dripping with water from the shaft, and told them firmly and earnestly what they were endeavouring to do.

This ugly mood which stirred some of the crowd was referred to by Mr. Coulson at the inquest reported in the 'Newcastle Courant" when he said " The public were getting very uneasy" at the unavoidable delays in the progress of the rescue work.

In the midst of it all Coulson had a brain-wave. Let them see for themselves he said. Let the crowd of men appoint two from their number to go down the shaft and see the state of things. The management adopted this suggestion and the men fell into line with it.

Accordingly, Charlie Gallagher and Jack McLeod were picked to go down. They were good practical pitmen, would kow-tow to nobody, and would give an honest report. They changed into their pit clothes and were lowered down the shaft in the loop. They were, in effect, pioneers of a local custom that was to become more widely adopted at the pits of the North, namely, the custom of appointing local inspectors to act on behalf of the men.

The crowd was at first pacified by this arrangement. But after Charlie and Jack had been away for some time they began to wonder at the delay. Surely they weren't all this time merely crawling through the hole in the obstruction at the Yard Seam and coming back to report ! Had something happened to them ?

Gradually, feelings were once more inflamed into a frenzy of impatient concern. Reid reports :

> While they were away, the dense mass of watchers were in a perfect agony of impatience. Looking down at them from a small bridge running from one platform to another, such a scene is presented as defies description—The crowd, moving madly in a body, like caged hyaenas, are swaying to and fro by an irresistible impulse. Now and then someone amongst them cries out in hoarse tones of discontent, and asks where the men are who have gone down. Someone

replies from the bridge that they have not yet come up, and again an agonised shudder runs through the people. At last, however, the deputation returns. In a moment a deadly silence reigns, and a sea of upturned faces is revealed by the flare of the watch-fires. One of the two men stepped forward and said in clear, distinct tones "Men, we have been told there is stythe at the bottom. Now we've been there, and there is none. There's water enough to drown a man, but no stythe". A low sound that can better be compared to a growl than to anything else, came from the crowd . . .

After this Mr. George Baker Forster, on behalf of the management stepped forward to comment on the report of the deputation. Doubtless, the men were right in what they had reported, that there was no evidence of stythe at the time they were down. Nevertheless, he feared there was some stythe. A man in the crowd shouted "Is it true the men jowled yesterday morning?" Mr. Forster replied that they had, for the sinker Davy Wilkinson had told him so, and Davy would not tell a lie.

Further questions and answers followed, and a demand was made that periodical announcements should be given from the platform indicating what progress, if any, had been made. Hence it was agreed that Mr. Humble, the resident viewer, should himself report once every two hours. This seemed to content the crowd and they once more lapsed into silence.

Mr. Humble kept his word. He reported at the expiration of two hours, but it was a cautious report couched in very general terms. The sinkers had, as they were already aware, holed through the rubbish just enough to squeeze a man through; the work was going on favourably and they were now enlarging the hole. There was a fair hope of the next shift getting on better still . . .

The crowd growled again. Mr. Humble was doing his honest best but it was obvious that what he had to say did not by any means satisfy the people who hungered for news. His report was interrupted with a volley of shouted questions—"What about the stythe?" yelled one man with a powerful voice.

"I asked no questions, and I heard no complaints", was Humble's cautious reply.

A shrill, high-toned female voice next pierced the air :
"Are they still alive?"

But any answer to that one was drowned by a chorus of
exclamations from the crowd :

"Oh, they don't know that, woman!"

Poor fellows, says Reid, the momentary rebellion of last
night has entirely subsided and they are once more passive and
uncomplaining. It is a bitter night, he adds, and the snow is
lying on the ground and flying through the air. But no one
will move away and there is hardly a woman in the hamlet who
is not on the spot.

Reid's remarks about the behaviour of the women recall
Dr. Thomas Hodgkin's account with regard to this.

The poor women, he tells us, could not be induced to take
any rest and hardly any food until their husbands' bodies were
brought back to them. Many remained on the pit-heap night
and day, and those who did stay at home would just sit staring
into the fire in blank sorrow, except when some neighbour or
visitor came in to rouse them from their stupor. This was after
the worst was known. He quotes a workman as saying to him
that it was pitiful to see them spending the whole day between
the clock and the door, just standing at the door straining their
eyes towards the pit-heap to see if he was coming from it, and
then reckoning by the clock how many hours he must have been
in the pit already. Furthermore, says Hodgkin, they simply
would not go to bed at night, "Just think how terrible it would
be if I was asleep when they brought **him** home!"

An incident is told of three women neighbours (they were
by now three widows) who sat through one night together for
company. At midnight there was a knock on the door. It was
a man dressed respectably in black. He came from Bishop
Auckland. Apparently a local preacher, his was a spiritual visi-
tation. He was aware of these long unsleeping vigils, so, as one
of the women said, he read to us "a deal of very nice chapters"
from the scriptures. And in the morning at 7 o'clock, after

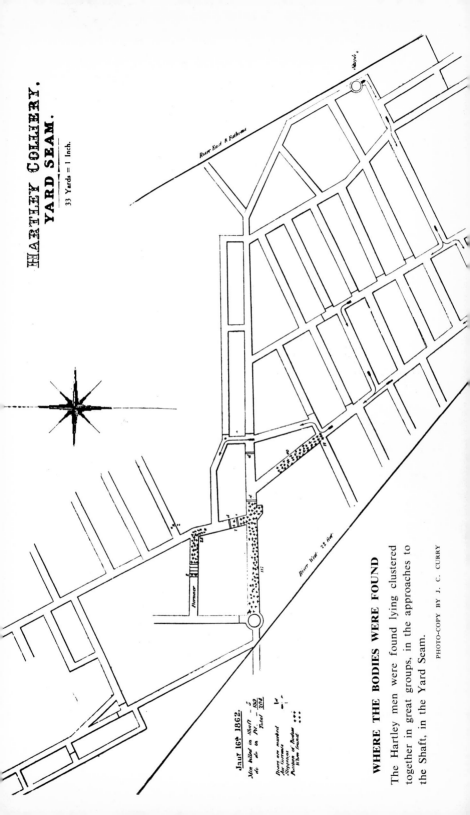

HARTLEY COLLIERY.
YARD SEAM.

33 Yards = 1 Inch.

River East 8 Fathoms

River West 22 feet

Jany 16th 1862.

Men killed in Shaft — 5
do do in Pit — 199
Total — 204

Doors are marked
Air Currents
Stoppings
Position of Bodies
When found

WHERE THE BODIES WERE FOUND

The Hartley men were found lying clustered together in great groups, in the approaches to the Shaft, in the Yard Seam.

PHOTO-COPY BY J. C. CURRY

ANNOUNCING THE NAMES OF THE DEAD

Robert Turnbull announcing to the great crowd the names of the dead as each coffin is brought forth from the pit.

PHOTO-COPY BY J. C. CURRY

READING THE QUEEN'S LETTER

Here Queen Victoria's letter is being read in a Hartley home. This is the second of the pair of pictures donated by Miss Garrigan for reproduction in this book.

having been given a little bread and butter and tea, he set off to walk back to Bishop Auckland.

We can well imagine the local preacher reading one of his "very nice chapters" from the scriptures . . .

Let not your heart be troubled ; ye believe in God, believe also in me. In my Father's house are many mansions; if it were not so I would have told you. I go to prepare a place for you—

At that moment the preacher looked up from his Bible. The attention of the women was likewise distracted by men's voices calling to each other in the street, for this unsleeping village knew no difference between night and day. Then it was quiet again and the preacher continued . . .

And if I go and prepare a place for you, I will come again and receive you unto myself, that where I am, there ye may be also.

Jesus saith, I am the way, the truth and the life; no man cometh unto the Father but by me.

I will not leave you comfortless ; I will come to you,

Peace I leave with you, my peace I give unto you; not as the world giveth, give I unto you.

Let not your heart be troubled, neither let it be afraid . . .

Meanwhile there was drama again at the pit. It happened at four o'clock on this wintry Tuesday morning, perhaps as our friend from Bishop Auckland was reading from the scriptures not far away.

The weary routine of working and watching was going on as usual when there happened, quite suddenly, what Reid describes as "an incident of a truly appalling nature".

A man rushed up to the platform and cried out in a loud voice, "All the men are alive; they've got the shaft clear, they're all safe!"

The sleepy-eyed watchers were galvanised into life instantly. A rush was made to the platform and the mouth of the pit. But the report proved false. The hopes, so cruelly re-awakened, were dashed down once more.

How this mad idea originated nobody knew. And there was no time to check up on it. For just as suddenly another crisis arose. The banksmen listening at the top of the pit received a distress signal from far below :

"Bend up the jack! Gas . . . "

The alarming news spread like wild-fire. The crowd was roused again. To use Reid's term they moved madly like caged hyaenas.

And in the dark of that winter morning scenes of great distress were witnessed. One sinker was brought up in the loop and staggered to the cabin supported by two comrades. Other sinkers were hauled out of the pit, but these had to be carried one after another, wet and limp and unconscious to the black-smith's shop. There in that make-shift, dingy and incongruous "emergency ward", local doctors worked with anxious concern to revive them. And there, amidst the chains and the hammers and the anvils, brave men were gradually recalled to life, and they ere long, felt constrained to resume their battle once more.

PART THREE

The Abandonment of Hope

Chapter 1

JOURNEY'S END—"A VAST GOLGOTHA"

It was obvious from the casualties amongst the sinkers that the pit was full of gas. And since that was so, there was now no hope of finding any survivors amongst the entombed men—that indeed proved to be the case, but let us look back for a while at the state of things prevailing before the dead were reached, the state of things described at the end of the last chapter when the gas was playing havoc with the sinkers.

It appears that much of the material blocking the shaft had fallen away to a lower level, and, like the uncorking of a bottle, the deadly mine gas was released, overcoming the men as they worked in the shaft.

Reid speaks of the effect of the gas on the sinkers. In addition to his account of those taken to the blacksmith's shop, he describes one sinker who was so ill that he was straightway removed in an ambulance elsewhere. So bad was he that, "He seemed to be in a deadly sleep. His face was pale, his eyes shut, and his hands lying listlessly before him. Merely to look at him, it might easily have been supposed that his was a lifeless body."

The doctors from Hartley and the adjoining districts worked hard to restore these victims. Their names are given as Doctors Davison, Ward, Nicholson and Ambrose. The sinkers who suffered most from the gas were William Coulson (son of the master sinker), Richard Wilson, Richard Dickson, John Little and Matthew Dunn.

The excitement amidst the crowd was now intense. Mr. Coulson, senior, and his right-hand man George Emmerson, made an attempt to go down the shaft to explore the position, but they were driven back by the gas with all speed and it was reluctantly decided to suspend operations for the time being.

Mr. Coulson, senior, referred to this experience at the inquest. He spoke of the sudden discharge of gas; that his men were using common candles which the gas made to burn brighter; that several of his men were brought to bank speechless, his own son among them; that when he, Coulson, senior, went down the shaft he found so much gas that it was lying four fathoms above the High Main Seam. Hence Coulson would not allow any more men to go "through that hole by the pumps". There followed a consultation with Mr. T. E. Forster and Mr. G. B. Forster, and a decision was arrived at that nothing more be done until brattice-cloth was installed in the shaft with a view to improving the ventilation.

The consultation which took place between Mr. Coulson and the viewers naturally turned to the nature of the gas which was being discharged. It was agreed that it was carbonic oxide, a deadly gas, which was thought to have been produced by the continued burning of the furnace in the pit. Having decided on the installation of the brattice-cloth it was soon realised that the stock held at Hartley was insufficient for the purpose, so a telegram was sent to Seaham Colliery asking for a supply. This was readily forthcoming, was quickly despatched by train, and the colliery saddler at Hartley set to work to stitch it up as required.

Although the gas episode came as a profound shock to the majority of the crowd, it was known to a few people that there had been evidence of it on the previous night. The sinker Davy Wilkinson, was the first to get a real whiff of the gas. He it was who made the hole through the rubbish with his shovel, and, peering into the darkness below, inhaled a quantity of the gas which so nearly killed some of his comrades soon afterwards. Davy was brought to bank at once and "staggered about like a drunken man" until the doctors brought him round.

After the first few gas casualties it was deemed advisable that greater caution should be exercised about entering the shaft. A cat was used to test the state of the air. Reid tells us that it was lowered down the shaft and when it was hauled up again some time later it was found to be "stupid and silly, hardly able to stand and seemed intoxicated."

George Cooke, the local poet, referred to this experiment in a simple verse which ran :

>A cat is lowered down to give
>An idea if a man could live;
>When brought to bank it was detected
>Poor pussy's limbs were much affected.

As the men pushed on with the fixing of the brattice-cloth, they were, of course, badly affected by the gas in the process, but as each portion was completed, conditions gradually improved.

What with the crises over the gas and one thing and another, someone discovered that the promised two-hourly bulletin had not been observed. So once more feeling in the crowd was aroused. Two o'clock in the morning as it was, that did not deter the crowd from calling for Mr. George Baker Forster and demanding to be given the latest intelligence.

In consequence, Mr. Forster addressed them. He spoke of the progress that had been made. That seemed to satisfy them somewhat. And Reid, who is very critical of the crowd when he feels it is justified, nevertheless gives expression to profound sympathy when he says, "They have waited another night, and, as may well be imagined, they are worn down to little more than shadows. Now, however, they seem to know and expect, the worst. God help them all!"

They had not long now to wait for the confirmation of their fears. On Wednesday morning at half-past eleven, news came to bank that workmen's tools had been found. It appeared that the sinker George Emmerson had pushed his way into the furnace drift connecting the shaft with the Yard Seam and made the discovery.

There was, it was said, a deathly stillness in that ghostly cavern :

Not a sound of any kind, however did he perceive. After looking by the flickering light of his candle for a short time he found two axes, a saw and a 'back-skin', evidence that the poor wretches had been labouring at that spot in endeavouring to effect their own deliverance.

Emmerson saw other tools and observed that the obstructing timbers had been cut and hacked as far as it was possible for anyone to reach them from below. He was about to explore still more of the drift when he felt himself being overcome by the gas. So grasping the few tools already mentioned he dragged himself back with difficulty to the shaft where two of his colleagues were anxiously awaiting his return. Even those two men, Davison and Burn, were "much affected by the great heat and stythe." The tools Emmerson brought out were then carefully examined for marks (for every miner in those days had his "ken-mark" on his gear) and they were found to belong to two of the entombed deputy-overmen, namely John Sharp and Thomas Ternent.

The next and most important stage in the unfolding of this drama was the finding of the bodies. It was Bill Adams a miner and a volunteer rescue worker from Cowpen, who first found them. Bill had a nickname "London Will." Because of this a report got about that the first man to reach the bodies was a London diver. Nothing could be more false than this says Reid and he goes on, "Adams was the first man to ascertain the actual occurrence of the most appalling, sudden calamity which the British Isles has known for many years. He goes under the cognomen of 'London Will' and so the mistake appears to have arisen."

Undaunted by the failures of the men on previous shifts, Bill Adams was determined to push into the Yard Seam. He was accompanied by two marrows, Robert Wilson from Backworth, and Thomas Cousins, with Bill Adams leading the way. They went through the "clack-door" and crawled along by the pumps to the furnace. There they found the first two bodies of the entombed men. Of course, the furnace fire was out by now, but it was found that the two bodies lying there were badly burned, evidently in their frantic efforts to escape from the death pit over the red-hot fire bars.

The rest of the heroic journey undertaken by Bill Adams and his marrows is described by Reid as follows :

> Pushing their way along at great danger to themselves, for the air was very bad, they managed to get to the long-sought Yard Seam. Here they opened a ventilating door and found more bodies strewn in all directions. Walking over them they came to another door which they also opened, and when they got through, they found the bodies, to use Adams's own words, 'thicker and faster'. In all the ghastly company not one spark of precious life remained. All had lain down and died. The smell was dreadful, and, as they had learned all that was wanted, the brave fellows came back again. As Adams himself said, 'It was a heartbreaking sight' and he added, 'No one need blame anybody for the delay, for it was an awful dangerous road along which we went.'

When the news of all this was reported at the pit-head many painful scenes followed. Reid remarks that, "At last the long-cherished hopes have forever vanished and there is a revulsion of feeling which words will not describe."

The pioneering work done by Bill Adams was followed by that of others. Mr. Humble went down accompanied by Mr. Hall, a viewer from Trimdon. They too suffered severely from the bad air of the pit. They were given some tea, Humble meanwhile exclaiming in heartrending accents about the dead.: ."Oh dear ! Oh dear !, so many of my fellow creatures dead. Oh, my canny fellows!" They had been right into the Yard Seam and had found all the men and boys. They were all dead. They were lying not far from the shaft, waiting for the help which never came. They were lying side by side, tiny pit boys clinging to their fathers. The pit-ponies' corn bins were empty, but corn was found in the pockets of some of the men. Near where they lay a pit pony was found dead but untouched.

It now became necessary to break this sad news, officially, to the waiting crowd. The difficult task was undertaken by Mr. John Taylor, the colliery viewer from Backworth. A great hush descended on the crowd as he cleared his throat to speak. Quietly and sympathetically he told of the tragic discoveries. There were lots of corpses but not a living soul had been found.

"Have the sinkers been as far as the Low Main Staple?" cried one man.

They hadn't as yet, Mr. Taylor replied. He appealed for them to be patient a little longer. The sinkers had gone as far as they could with safety. It's no use, he said forcefully, throwing away good lives to obtain dead bodies. Finally, he requested those present to communicate this intelligence to any of the relatives and friends who were not present.

Despite all the dark forebodings of this tragic end, Mr. Taylor's announcement fell like a thunderbolt. There was a crushing finality about it. And it told many of those present that they were now widows, orphans or childless. The news spread like wildfire through the desolate village, and, as Reid puts it, "the last, uncertain, flickering flame of hope was now finally quenched."

Nevertheless, the work must still go on. But it went on without that spirit and zest which had hitherto characterized the rescue effort. Preparations were made to improve the circulation of the air in the pit, and to make safe the shaft and the roadways so that the bodies could be brought from the pit, and the working places more thoroughly explored.

Even after the announcement of the finding of the bodies conditions were still very bad indeed. The openings into the workings which had been made, might at any moment close like a grave. The stythe in the shaft was very bad and men were being drawn up every minute ill from its effects. As to the shaft, stone kept falling from the sides, and at one place just above the Yard Seam, instead of a circular shaft 12 feet 6 inches across, Reid likened it to a quarry 20 to 30 feet in diameter because of the earth which had fallen away.

The crowd around the pit, at first stunned by Mr. Taylor's announcement, gradually bestirred themselves to fresh life. This took the usual form of a renewed demand for "local inspectors" of their own choice to go down the pit. This was felt in official quarters to be useless. No good purpose could possibly be served by such a deputation. However, the management understood the mood of the men and so permission was granted.

Two men were chosen from the mighty crowd present. They were the brothers Richard and Thomas Boyd of North Seaton. They readily volunteered for the difficult task, changed into their pit clothes, went swinging down on the rope and remained below for about two hours.

It seemed a long two hours to the waiting crowd but eventually Dick and Tom came back to report. Dick seemed to suffer the more from the effects of the gas, but after a cup of tea and a sip of brandy he was somewhat restored. He told the crowd as he gasped for breath, what he and his brother had seen. The sinkers had holed through from the shaft into the furnace drift right enough but there wasn't much room there yet. Crawl on your belly, that's what you had to do in some places. In fact they'd got stuck a canny few times. They had passed over the fire-bars of the furnace and had seen the bodies of the two men lying there. Both were awful swollen. Then they went on to the Yard Seam, and round the workings. It was near the shaft where most of the bodies were lying, about 150 of them, all lying together. All looked as if they had lain down and gone to sleep. They must have been dead for some time, and there was a bad smell in the place where they lay. They stayed as long as they dare and Dick declared that he was so overcome with the bad air that had his brother not caught him and dragged him away to the shaft, he would certainly have collapsed amongst the dead in the pit.

Meanwhile the great crowd listened with silent resignation. Only a cough or two had been heard while Dick Boyd was speaking. There was none of that growling anger which had greeted some of the previous reports. These two men had looked into the face of death, and in language honest and home-spun, they told what they had seen.

And when they had finished, the men in the crowd sighed heavily, and the women sobbed quietly into their shawls.

There was never a moment now without its excitement at the top of the pit. Scarcely had the Boyd brothers reported than a new sensation engaged the attention of the crowd. A sinker was brought to bank in a fighting mood! Such was the strange effect of the gas upon him that he put up his fists in a sparring attitude and shocked bystanders by trying to give the doctors a few upper cuts! It was an incredible performance. Here is Reid's account :

> We have just seen one man brought up who seemed to be raging drunk. He offered to fight, tried to take off his coat, and struggled violently when they endeavoured to hold him. After a while he became quiet and sat down, seeming to awake from a dream.

Dr. Davison himself confirms this story. It was he who was in constant attendance at the Hartley pit throughout the tragedy, and in March, 1862, he sent a letter to the **Lancet** in which he analysed the effects of the gas upon those who died, and the others who in varying degrees suffered from it. The letter is given in full in an appendix to this book but it is of interest here to mention that Dr. Davison does indeed confirm Reid's story of the "fighting sinker." He says :

> Another man was very violent and excited, wishing to fight the medical men in attendance—very much like the effects of chloroform.

During this day a telegram was received which had been sent at the behest of Queen Victoria, who was anxious to be informed as to how things were going at Hartley. It was received by Mr. Charles Carr, the Hartley Viewer and was as follows :—

> **General Grey, Osborne, to the Viewer, New Hartley Colliery, Shields.**
>
> The Queen is most anxious to hear that there are hopes of saving the poor people in the colliery, for whom her heart bleeds.

Mr. Carr sent the following reply :—

> There are still faint hopes of the men or a portion of them, being recovered alive.

That was despatched in the afternoon but by the evening it was necessary to send a second telegram from Hartley which said that upwards of one hundred had been found dead and that now there was no hope of saving anyone.

At nine o'clock that night (Wednesday) another wave of discontent was made manifest when a spontaneous mass meeting took place at the pit-head. It was Mr. Coulson's method of working which was the target for criticism. The critics said he was not going the right way about it or the bodies would have been long since recovered.

Mr. Coulson once more addressed the noisy and bewildered crowd. He spoke as a man whose knowledge of the problem was unrivalled, but there was in his utterance an undoubted sympathy and understanding of the emotional strain which motivated the critics in his audience. "I want nothing" he said, "but the common end which you all seek. Why should I want to prolong this agony? It does me no good. I'll tell you this— if there's a man-jack among you willing to tackle this difficult job, let him come forward now. I'll gladly give it up to him— if he can manage it."

There was a chorus of indignant "Noes" at this last proposition. It was apparent that Coulson had won their support for his policy which was not to rush in recklessly to try to drag the dead bodies to the shaft, but to restore the ventilation, and to make safe the shaft and the roadways. That would take at least fifteen hours, but better that delay than to throw away more lives.

It must be admitted that it was not just the hotheads in the crowd who voiced their disapproval of Mr. Coulson. There were a few informed people who openly said his methods were wrong. For instance a letter to the **Colliery Guardian** dated February 8th, 1862, suggested that a heavy ram should have been dropped down the shaft to clear the blockage. In a feature marking the centenary of the disaster the **Colliery Guardian** of February 8th 1962, quotes the letter as follows :—

WISE AFTER THE EVENT

An old sinker, in a letter to **Colliery Guardian,** criticises the procedure adopted in reaching the doomed men in Hartley Colliery.

I have no doubt the sinkers and Mr. Coulson did all they could in prosecuting their arduous and unsatisfactory task to save the lives of their fellow-men, with a shaft above their heads in a most dangerous state, caused by the falling 'beam' ripping out the main brattice, cribs, cleaving deals, and pump collarings. It is quite apparent a great mistake was committed by attempting to remove the debris in the shaft to the main coal seam. Had a ram been used to force the rubbish from the bucket and clack doors scaffolds, the shaft would have been cleared, and the lives of the poor fellows saved, I have not the slightest doubt. It is strange that it did not strike someone that material falling down the shaft was certain to collect at points where the shaft is necessarily contracted in size by the placing of bucket and clack door scaffolds. That the shaft was open is satisfactorily proved by one of the sinkers turning his shovel round when the stythe forced him out of the pit.

The storm against Coulson at the pit once more blew over, and a strange calm descended upon the place. Many of the watchers, having at last lost heart, now drifted away from the pit for the first time since the disaster occurred. Several of the medical men departed leaving two of their number on duty to meet any emergency. Most of the viewers from the other collieries had also gone home. In consequence of all this an uncanny lull prevailed. True, the work went on but all the drive and spirit concerning its progress was absent. As Reid remarked. "There is nothing now to hope for and the men are, of course, very unwilling to risk their lives in merely seeking to gain the dead bodies of the lost ones."

This then was journey's end. Despite the fact that there was so much more work to be done before the bodies could be brought to bank, it was, nevertheless, journey's end. It was the end when Bill Adams led the way, staggering, sweating and gasping for breath into that ghostly sepulchre where so many of the men lay dead.

As he picked his way over the bodies by candlelight, it was to Bill an eerie and a spine-chilling experience. Scores of dead men in their pit clothes lay stretched along the rolleyway four abreast; on and on they lay into the shadows beyond the reach of the feeble light shed by his candle. Indeed by the light of that flickering flame which he thrust before him as he went, he was uncertain at times whether it was substance or shadow which loomed up as if to impede his path. Only when he stooped lower with his light could he perceive more closely the grim reality of being face to face with death.

It was strange to Bill to learn how different in death were the members of this ghostly company. Many of those lying there appeared to be in a deep, deep, sleep. There were those whose expressions were so composed as to suggest that they had escaped to some secret heaven of their own creation, and were oblivious of this underworld chamber of horrors with its rough stone sides and its pit-prop roof supports. And on their countenances there was a serenity in death which even the grime of the pit could not efface. Indeed it was one of this sublime company who had left a written message telling of the prayer meeting which they had held.

But how different many of the others. Their faces were greatly swollen and their features distorted. A bloody fluid oozed from their mouths and nostrils, and their eyes stared wildly, as if some hidden terror had possessed their souls in torment in their last hours of life in the pit, and had left its mark, frozen into these repulsive masks of death. Moreover the smell from their bodies was nauseating in the extreme . . .

It was fortunate that Bill Adams staggered back to the shaft when he did.

Yes, this was journey's end—one "Vast Golgotha."

Chapter 2

PREPARATIONS FOR A SAD "RESURRECTION"

One of Mr. Reid's most telling phrases in which he describes the raising of the dead from the Hartley Pit was that it resembled "some unholy premature resurrection."

The old scriptural idea of the graves opening and the dead being raised, was doubtless at the back of his mind when he used that simile to portray what actually happened at Hartley.

And Reid was right. It was indeed a grimly impressive business this "resurrection" of the dead. There has surely never been anything quite like it in the whole history of coal-mining.

As we have already seen, Coulson got his way about having things put to rights before the "lifting" operation was begun. Colliery joiners made "cribs" which were circular frames of wood to form bases for building up the shaft sides. Heavy falls of stone continued to take place, and on one occasion a stone one ton in weight crashed down narrowly missing the men at work below.

As if there were not troubles enough, a fire started amongst some of the timbers near the shaft but this was quickly got under control.

Then again the alarm was raised that the water in the Low Main was rising fast and it was feared the bodies might be lost if it reached the Yard Seam. It was, of course, true that the water was rising in the bottom-most seam of the pit since the pumping engine had broken down, but there was no immediate danger of losing the bodies which had been reached after so great an effort.

Troubles seemed to come not as single spies but in battalions. At nine o'clock on Friday morning the gas broke out again, causing casualties. The gas seemed to come chiefly from the Low Main Seam, and one way of tackling it was to put a platform, a kind of lid, across the shaft just below the Yard Seam

THE FUNERAL PROCESSION

Part of the Funeral Procession which, in all, was four miles long!

BURIAL AT EARSDON

This was a most moving occasion. There was no room in the old churchyard for so many bodies, so a hole was broken through the churchyard wall and a neighbouring field taken over for the purpose. Gravediggers toiled nonlevel, thus sealing it off. Above this a swinging scaffold, sus-pended on ropes, was devised for the shaft workers as they laboured to secure the sides, and to improve the brattice partition.

In the expectation of the raising of the bodies from the pit hosts of visitors poured back into Hartley, and we are told that the "hot-pie men" did a roaring trade. The various ministers of religion, including the Lord Bishop of Durham himself, went from door to door in their endeavours to console the bereaved. The Lord Mayor of Newcastle came to Hartley. Family mourners from other parts of the country came, and there were many of these, for nearly every house had suffered a bereave-ment, and the white blinds of death were displayed at every window.

Needless to say, there were many painful scenes on the re-union of relatives under such tragic circumstances.

Evidence of the interest taken by the country generally is shown by the fact that reporters from the **Times,** the **Morning Chronicle,** the **Mining Journal,** as well as the reporters from the Newcastle papers were in attendance to cover the disaster story. Moreover, two artists from the **Illustrated London News** made a number of sketches some of which are reproduced in this book.

The close sympathy of Queen Victoria with the sufferers at Hartley was again shown by the receipt on Thursday of a tele-gram expressing her sorrow. The Queen's message was as follows :

Sir Charles Phipps to Messrs. Carr—

The Queen has been deeply affected by the dreadful news from Hartley. Her Majesty feels the most sincere sympathy for the poor widows and orphans. What is doing for them ? I will write by tonight's post.

In the absence of Messrs. Carr, the following reply was sent by Mr. T. E. Forster :

Measures have been arranged for the temporary relief of the widows and orphans, and a public meeting is to be held in New-castle tomorrow to arrange for a permanent relief fund. There are 406 women and children left destitute.

In the numbering of the dependent children those over the age of 16 were not counted.

In view of the unfortunate scenes which had taken place on the pit-heap, it was felt by responsible elements amongst both management and men that the platform ought to be carefully guarded against intruders. Hence the men on guard there were very vigilant in the exercise of their duty, carefully preventing all save those whose presence was absolutely necessary, from going on to the platform. This led to some amusing scenes. Numbers of well-dressed people kept coming up, hoping by "a carelessly assumed effrontery" to be able to pass the vigilant janitors. They were disappointed, however, for the keepers of the entrances were no respecters of persons. While the meanest clad workman who had a job to do, was allowed to pass, the fashionably attired idler, however high and mighty, was unceremoniously turned away.

Meanwhile, the mass meetings already referred to as a feature of Hartley's present way of life became even more frequent. And a leader of men came to the fore whose stature increased with each new day of crisis. He was Robert Turnbull, a pitman from Cowpen, whom Reid described as "a tall, singular-looking man with long curling ringlets and a shaggy beard."

Turnbull seemed always to preside at these meetings and his task was by no means easy in view of the angry mood shown by some of his audience. After the abusive attack on Mr. Coulson, Turnbull addressed the meeting and it was doubtless his persuasive eloquence which was responsible for the passing of a resolution expressing confidence in Coulson and his men. Now that the hour was near for the lifting of the bodies Turnbull appealed to the people not to rush the shaft but to be patient and orderly.

But despite Robert Turnbull's earnest appeals there were men in the audience who kept demanding that more "local inspectors" be allowed down the pit. This request was, however, resisted as it was calculated to stop the work, as, indeed, it had done for some hours on a previous occasion.

Perhaps the resultant feeling of frustration was worked upon by the more vocal element in the crowd for Reid tells us, "Dreadful scenes are occurring, fathers coming to the shaft, almost frantic to seek their children, wives wailing for their husbands, and sons for their parents. It is a most painful scene now that despair has finally settled down upon it."

The above words are quoted from Reid's report sent to his newspaper at 10-30 on Thursday morning, but by noon, he felt compelled to despatch another report in which he enlarged upon the conduct of a section of the crowd. This report is headed **Serious Disturbance Among the Miners**, and says, that the behaviour was "scandalously bad" entailing danger and delay to Coulson and his men. The majority of the people in the crowd, he says, were long-suffering, quiet and patient, but the noisy element were "wickedly unreasonable." "Bring out the dead!" they cried. They wanted the sinkers to go for the bodies without a moment's delay and bring them to the surface, which, if carried out was simply throwing away good lives after bad.

Then Reid goes on to review and to justify the position of Coulson in this matter. He and his men had striven hard and had taken great risks, but now the case was different. They had succeeded in satisfying everybody that not a living thing of any description was to be found in the pit and the only object to be gained was the speedy and decent burial of the 199 corpses then decaying in the Yard Seam. No doubt this was a most important object, but was it worth risking an additional life to attain ? "Surely the annals of the Hartley New Pit are already black enough!"

But the militant elements in the crowd had no regard for such considerations. "Shoot Coulson!" they cried angrily, and threatened to take the whole affair into their own hands.

One man, concerning whom Reid says he could say no harsh words since he had lost four sons in the disaster jumped upon the platform and acted in a manner which proved that grief had completely unhinged his mind. Had he not been restrained he would undoubtedly have thrown himself headlong down the shaft. Others were nearly as bad. In these circumstances, Mr,

Coulson told the people once and for all that if this kind of thing continued he would be compelled to withdraw his men altogether. The danger of the work was being wantonly and uselessly increased by such behaviour. He let it be known how deeply hurt he was by such demonstrations.

It was as a result of these scenes that the mass meeting above-mentioned took place. It was held at the side of the pit-heap between the colliery village and the engine house. A dense mass of people, nearly all men, was gathered there, and as Reid looked across at them he said one might have fancied that some country preacher was earnestly engaged in holding forth. Such was the impression created by the eloquence of Robert Turnbull the pitman from Cowpen. He spoke to the men in a firm but kindly manner. Order must be kept. The dead would be restored to their relatives as quickly as possible. Anxious relatives had put to him specific points, and about these he gave definite assurances. He assured them for instance that the lids on the coffins would not be screwed down until all the bodies had been identified as far as possible.

In the working out of some procedure for identifying the dead and making the results known to the waiting crowd, Mr. Turnbull was the go-between linking the management with the men. For instance, the official side said that Mr. Humble, the viewer, should identify each body, write the deceased's name on a slip of paper, and put it in the open coffin.

But the crowd had other ideas. They had to be democratic even concerning matters of death. So an "Identification Committee" of twelve men was appointed. And it was requested that each body be brought up to the barrier on the platform, and there, in front of the waiting multitude, the name of each dead man be called out so that the relatives might come forward to gaze upon, and claim their own respective dead.

Then another mass meeting was held. And again Robert Turnbull occupied the chair. This time the subject was the setting up of a relief fund to make provision for the dependants. Once more there was work for a committee whose job it was to go from door to door to ascertain the true position as to need. Subsequently, the committee reported that there were declared to be 406 dependants. Meanwhile, other authorities were making arrangements for the convening of meetings on Thursday and Friday both of which were to be held in Newcastle to which this local report about the number of dependants was to be submitted.

Friday came and with it another mass meeting at the pit-heap. The subject on this occasion concerned arrangements for the burial of the dead. Rev. R. E. Mason, the incumbent of Earsdon, addressed the meeting. It was a sad thing, he said, but there was not room in the churchyard for the burial of all the dead at Hartley. He had spoken to His Grace the Duke of Northumberland, who was willing to grant the use of the field adjacent to the churchyard for burial purposes, provided the bereaved were consulted on the matter. A committee of six was thereupon appointed to consult the feelings of relatives.

Just after the conclusion of the above meeting Robert Turnbull mounted the platform close to the pit-head to report on these and other arrangements when there was an outburst of strong feeling from a dissatisfied section of the crowd. In one of the incidents connected with this, a local character, Billy McKee by name, aggressively demanded to be allowed to go down the pit. Billy, whose father and brother were down the pit, went on to the platform in a very excited state, and threatened to jump down the shaft, but he was caught just in time and led away.

In the early evening of Friday, news of the afternoon meeting in Newcastle reached Hartley, and Robert Turnbull convened another meeting to impart the knowledge in his possession concerning subscriptions received and other relief fund matters.

That same evening a rather surprising deputation waited upon Mr. Charles Carr, the Hartley Colliery viewer. They reported the decision of a mass meeting held the night before. The purport of this was that they, who had themselves lost so much by way of bereavement and the jobs by which they earned their daily bread, expressed deep sympathy with the coalowners in their great loss ! "Such a fact", comments Reid, "speaks volumes and is beyond all praise."

Yet another meeting was held that night to appoint two delegates to attend the big conference on pit safety which was to be held in Newcastle on the Saturday afternoon.

And so the corporate life of this closely-knit little community went on its way meeting problem by problem as it arose, animated by the spirit that they were indeed "members one of another."

But despite all their preoccupations however necessary they might be, with collective arrangements of one kind and another, the grim necessity of raising corpses from the pit and providing for their decent disposal was now to be faced in earnest.

Stern reminders concerning this task gradually increased. Mr. G. B. Forster engaged himself in getting together a stock of blankets, sheets, etc., for the purpose of holding the bodies, and another gentleman left for Newcastle to obtain additional supplies of such articles.

All the colliery carpenters in the district around Hartley were engaged all out on the making of coffins, but it was impossible for them to satisfy so great a demand, and many coffins had to be got from outside. The sawing and hammering went on around the clock.

Then the coffins began to arrive at the pit-head. Cart after cart laden with black coffins drew up and disgorged their contents as near the pit as possible. Reid refers to the melancholy sight which they presented. They, perhaps more than anything else, he says, visibly exhibit the terrible nature of the loss which has been sustained. It is a sad, a heart-rending sight, to stand beside a single coffin, he goes on, but here we see the gradual assembly of two hundred, each destined for an occupant ! They are indeed mute, black witnesses of death.

The next day, Friday, another consignment of coffins arrived. Reid, on the spot as usual, tells us about it and goes into detail about the coffins :

> One long country cart after another was drawn up at the stable door and unladen of the coffins which it bore. At last a climax was reached by the arrival of a special train conveying nothing but coffins made at a distance. These coffins were not of course highly polished, nor were they yet like those of the lesser catastrophe at

Burradon, mere white wooden boxes, nailed together in such a manner as hardly to be able to stand the slightest strain. All of them, though made of the commonest deal, were strong and substantial and were neatly and decently stained with the deepest black. There they stood in dismal piles, covering every inch of space and rising in tiers of three and four above the ground. The restless crowd was not long in discovering them, and they came in little groups and stood staring at them earnestly as though they expected some strange and terrible sight would be presented by their blackened sides.

Other preparations were meanwhile taking place. One hundred pairs of long-armed gloves for the use of those who must handle the dead, two huge barrels of chloride of lime with which to dust the bodies as they were brought up, and scores of shrouds.

And so the scene at the pit-head moved on to its grand climax. As dawn broke on Saturday there was a sense of great expectancy, as if a theatre curtain was about to be raised for the final act of a great tragic drama.

It had indeed been expected that the lifting of the bodies would begin in the dark hours of the night, for, as Reid tells us, the night itself was suitable for such a task, since a hoarse wind sullenly howled a solemn requiem over the sepulchre of the dead, and the rain fell in fitful gusts upon the flaring watch-fires. And all around men and women waited.

But it was not to be. Saturday's dawn broke bright and sunny. The pale-faced watchers could at last see signs of the fact that their long, drawn-out vigil was near its end.

Mr. Coulson, Mr. Forster and Mr. Humble made a last minute examination of the shaft and tested the state of the ventilation. A number of doctors assembled whose object it was to see that the bodies were properly coffined ere they left the pit-head. Members of the Identification Committee were given their allotted tasks, tasks in which they were greatly assisted by the sharpness of a lad from the token cabin, not more than 14 years of age, who seemed to know quite a lot of the dead.

All preparations having now been made, the first body was drawn to bank, watched with the utmost interest by all concerned.

Chapter 3

BRINGING UP THE BODIES

There is something about the various aspects of the Hartley story which justifies the use of the adverb "superlative". Whether it be the patient resignation of the relatives of those entombed, or the heroism of the sinkers, it calls for language expressive of the highest praise.

And the same can be said of Reid's reporting of the bringing up of the bodies out of the pit. It is a remarkably graphic piece of writing.

Throughout this book I have not hesitated to put in a quotation from Reid's authentic record as the man on the spot, but for the purposes of the present chapter, the words must, almost exclusively, be his. For no one writing at this distance could hope to recapture the agonizing essence of that poignant moment of time in our industrial history. Nor could the language itself be bettered, for Reid's account is indeed a superlative piece of writing.

Let me explain at the outset that, at the last moment, a change of plan had been decided upon about the procedure to be followed in the raising of the dead. It had at first been thought possible to coffin the dead in the pit, but it was eventually realised that it would be awkward getting the coffins down and up that difficult shaft, and at best it would be an extremely slow business.

All along, says Reid, it had been announced that the coffins would be taken down the pit and the bodies placed in them there before being brought to the surface. About half-past ten therefore, when all other things were prepared, we, in common with most of the spectators began to watch for the disappearance of the first coffin down the shaft. Looking at that mysterious opening at the moment we saw that the ropes attached to both the "jack" and the "gin" were in motion. When, therefore, the order was given by Mr. Coulson, for a coffin to be moved nearer the shaft, we fully expected that in a moment it would disappear from our sight.

We were, however, destined to see a far more fearful spectacle. As the end of the rope drew near the surface, one of the men was seen riding upon the little sling in the rope in which the sinkers have so fearlessly ascended and descended. Just below him carefully attached to an iron chain, was a strange and hideous object which at first we could not recognise. In a moment, however, we saw that it was the stiffened form of one of the victims of the carbonic-oxide gas that was dangling in mid-air before us.

Straightway, he was landed on the platform. It was dreadful to look upon his skinny attenuated form which seemed so small beside the gigantic men gathered around. His almost fleshless hands were curiously marked in white and blue and his immobile features, and closed eyes denoted that he had slept even while treading the Valley of the Shadow of Death. He was thrown down upon an open shroud placed upon the ground, and while he was being rapidly rolled up in it, someone called out his name, which was methodically entered in a book by one man whilst another chalked it upon the lid of a coffin into which he was forthwith lifted.

Thus laden the coffin was placed upon a small rolley and pushed along the wooden bridge separating one portion of the pit-heap from another. At the further end when the name inscribed on the coffin was called out, someone stepped forward from among the dense crowd of waiters, and, claiming the body as that of a relative, placed it in a cart and conveyed it to the home which it had left in health and strength some ten days ago.

So quickly was all this done that the bystanders had scarcely had time to recover from the effects which it had produced upon them when another cry from the shaft mouth of "Stop the gin!" announced that another ghastly freight had arrived. It too was rolled unceremoniously down upon the platform, wrapped up in the winding sheet, placed in a coffin, and trundled along the bridge with marvellous rapidity. And it was not until it also had disappeared that we were able to ask the reason for this unexpected change of plan.

An explanation was given along the lines already indicated.

Then, as Reid watched the lifting operation he noticed something different on the next journey — two bodies were brought up together this time.

Once more standing by the shaft, he says, we saw the ropes gliding steadily upwards, this time bearing from below a double burden. Lashed together, face to face, we saw the bodies of two of the dead. Both wore upon their countenances an air of perfect repose, and while sitting upright in the sling where they were lashed, it was hard to see the difference between them and the iron-nerved "rider" who sat so composedly above them. When once, however, they were laid at our feet, the difference was all too plain to be seen. The spirit had fled forever from the bodies before us, and there was nothing but lifeless clay remaining.

Reid then sets on record a touching little scene which many another scribe might not have noticed. It followed the raising of the two bodies just mentioned and was as follows :

An old man, one of the carpenters engaged in bringing up the coffins, came up to this couple and knelt beside one of them, a strong fine-looking young man. With all the intense deep-seated earnestness of a father's love, he gently stroked the face and patted the hands of his son, for such the corpse once had been. It was only a few caresses that he gave but what volumes did they not speak ! And when he turned back to his work, with the scalding tears running down his cheeks, the heart must have been hard indeed that did not bleed acutely for his grief.

And so the work went on. A constant succession of "frightful burdens" were brought up from the pit. Men and boys of all ages and sizes were brought to bank. Some had died with a smile on their faces, others had been frowning in terror or anger. There were men of gigantic mould, still apparently engaged in a deadly struggle with the last adversary of death, and there were children weak and helpless, early doomed to toil in everlasting darkness, who had been found in the pit clasped in the arms of loving fathers. Hour after hour the work went on. One after another the bodies were dragged up out of the pit until it seemed "as if some unholy premature resurrection" was going on for which the Lord of Life and Death would certainly one day call upon us to account.

Despite the dreadful terrors of this scene at the centre of the stage, there were incidental happenings which caught Reid's eye—the constant hurrying to and fro of busy men, some carrying coffins, others spreading shrouds from the huge bales which lay around, and yet others who were thrusting the stiffened bodies into the unfitting coffins doubtless sometimes breaking bones in the process. One man, whilst engaged in this work never for a moment took from his mouth a short clay pipe; others, pausing for an instant from their labours, drained down the glasses of neat whisky which an active doctor administered to them; whilst over and above all, strange cries arose : "A longer coffin wanted here", "This body is far too small for such a big coffin", "Bring some more chloride of lime" and a hundred similar exclamations all adding to the confusion of the scene.

The men who were bringing up the bodies worked in shifts, and as this repulsive work was not liked by all the sinkers, some were compelled to remain at their posts longer than was good for them. The dreadful work went on for $17\frac{1}{2}$ hours and consequently most of it took place in the darkness of that January day and night. During that time piles of coffins were filled and borne away. Now and again Reid rivets our attention on the scene by producing for our benefit a kind of vivid flash-light photograph of the procedings.

At present, he says, the appearance of the platform is perfectly awful. In every direction it is lit up by watch-fires which cast a lurid glow over all the objects around them. Foremost amongst these is the woodwork of the shaft, and as we look at it we see emerging from the cimerian shade of the shaft first the "rider" wet and tired, and then an awful mass of limp bone and muscle, clad in the common pitman's dress, and dripping with water which has fallen upon it during its passage upwards. Thus, amidst hoarse cries, orders to "Bend down the jack" and exclamations of the names of the lost, the work goes on. And one body after another, neither delicately nor tenderly, for this is no time for lady's play, is thrust into its wooden cell.

Whilst all this was going on, down below the platform a great silent crowd anxiously waited. It strained eagerly to catch a glimpse of the operations being performed on the platform. They were all very quiet and orderly, these people, and were duly impressed with the solemnity of the occasion. Many had come to Hartley on foot from collieries all over the Northern counties, others were from the big towns and had been brought hither by the Blyth and Tyne Railway. In a mixed English crowd of this kind there might have been a rude jocularity, a rough and ready humour in evidence. But not here today at Hartley. In such close contact with Death, the utmost decorum was observed by all.

If we could imagine this setting at the Hartley Pit as a kind of revolving stage, we should be able to swing into our vision something that was happening at the other side of the pit-heap. A long wooden bridge separated the two portions, and at the other end of the bridge from that just described, another great crowd waited. This was not a crowd of mere spectators. These were relatives claiming their dead. Across this long wooden bridge the coffins, one after another, were trundled in quick succession. As each coffin was borne towards the crowd of relatives, our friend Robert Turnbull acted as a kind of Master of Ceremonies. It will be remembered that Turnbull was described by Reid as "a tall singular-looking man with long curling ringlets and a shaggy beard." With his powerful voice, Turnbull called out the name written in chalk upon the coffin lid. Then there was a sharp cry. Someone darted forward, and planting himself beside the coffin, the crowd opened, forming a lane down which the coffin was trundled to one of the numerous carts standing at the bottom of the hill.

Few were the mourners who followed the body once so full of love and life to the house it had once possessed. Occasionally, a wailing woman, generally some distant male relative who had come for the occasion, was all the retinue the corpse could command. Cart after cart moved towards the little village, and the dead were taken out and left in turn at almost every door.

But all the day through, it was heart-rending to see the bereaved women looking eagerly towards the colliery, waiting for the moment when they should possess the miserable consolation of once more looking upon the features of those whom they had lost.

It sometimes happened that a coffin bore the word "unknown" when it reached the bridge end. In such cases the lid was removed and the eager throng allowed to gather round earnestly to inspect the disfigured face. Often this resulted in painful recognition. But in several instances no one could claim the body, and the strange unwanted tenant of the coffin was removed to the small Primitive Methodist Chapel in the village.

All day-long and into the night this non-stop drama was enacted. As each body was brought up it was sprinkled with chloride of lime, for some of them were "much gone" and an "unbearable stench" proceeded from them. After the work had gone on for some time, Reid reported that the platform was white with chloride of lime, two barrels of which had by then been consumed.

Slowly, the tragic drama drew to its close. At four o'clock on this sad, winter Sunday morning, the overman in charge of the underground operations came out of the pit, spent and weary, and reported that he had been further into the workings than anybody else and had found the body of Jim Amour the back-overman, and that of his son. From this it was deduced that all the men must have got up the staple from the Low Main as the conscientious Amour would be certain not to leave until all the men he had in his charge were up before him.

It is worthy of note that there was no preference shown in the method of recovering the bodies. Each was taken up just

93

as he lay in relation to his proximity to the shaft. But towards the end the work became increasingly laborious and difficult. The further into the Yard Seam the body lay the more rough was the going and the more agonizingly strenuous the work of recovery. Some workers shrank in exhaustion unable to make further effort. And those who kept right on to the end of the road must have heaved a mighty sigh of relief when, at length, the last body was hauled, swaying, dangling and dripping wet, up that dark pit shaft of death.

Chapter 4

THE DAY OF THE GREAT FUNERAL

From the point of view of the weather the Sabbath morning of the 26th January, 1862 got out bright and beautiful.

New Hartley village was early astir as a busy day lay ahead for all concerned. It was the day of the Great Funeral.

This Sunday was in every sense different from the last. Then the battle to save lives was at its height, the fate of the entombed men was not known, and throughout the village excitement, toil, tension and hope were the order of the day.

Today it was different. The fate of the men was known. Women and children now knew that they were widows and orphans. There was a sadness of resignation. A black despair brooded over all.

Reid strolled up the village street that second Sunday morning after the disaster and reported on the desolation all too evident around him. Indeed only now after the dreadful preoccupations of the past ten days, did he have time to "size up" the village. Hartley, he said, is as unpicturesque as possible. It comprises two long rows of houses standing at right angles in the form of the letter "L", with a few small gardens on the other side of the muddy road in front.

The white blinds betokening death were displayed at every window. Looking in through the open door of every house there were coffins to be seen. In most instances they lay upon the large bed so characteristic of the pitman's dwelling. The bed was in every case hung with curtains of the purest white and the coffin itself generally had a spotless white cloth thrown over it. Sometimes the bed could not contain the coffins and then they were disposed on chairs beside it. Reid's story goes on :

> And so we passed up the row and saw two, three and four coffins all in one little room till at last, coming to the end house, we were appalled to see a perfect pile of them, only partially hidden by the

95

covering. **And, looking round we were informed that seven dead bodies lay in this cottage !** In every house women were sitting by the fire nursing their grief, and strong men, pale and dejected, were visibly suffering from the reaction of the excitement of the past week. It was a touching sight, and one calculated to cause the thoughtful man to ponder upon the mysterious way of Him who has thus permitted the destruction of a whole community.

Confirmation of Reid's account of the coffins in the cottages is given in George Cooke's poem written at the time of the disaster. But George also tells us the name of the family with the seven coffins :

> In every house there was the bed,
> And coffins black, with silent dead,
> We looked within the cottage doors,
> There lay the twos and threes and fours.
>
> The attention of the passers by
> Attracted, where so many lie,
> Crowds were seen to come and go
> Into the end house of the row.
>
> Lay seven coffins there behold
> With seven Liddles stiff and cold,
> I saw them piled up together
> Lying one upon another.

George Cooke also tells us of a house nearby—the sad case of Mrs. Oliver who lost a family of six :

> A little further down the row
> To Mrs. Oliver's I did go;
> Three on the bed, one on the floor,
> Two on a table near the door.

The reporter, Reid, visited the chapel. There it stood by the roadside between the pit and the village. A Primitive Methodist Chapel, it was described as a small and humble erection built in the style usual for such edifices.

Entering it, a sad sight was presented. The building had for the moment been adapted to serve as a mortuary in which the bodies of those who were "unknown" were left for identification.

One feels constrained to pause for a moment to reflect on this change of use of the little chapel. Here in this simple

Friday afternoon at half past one Edward Armstrong Thomas Gledson John Harding Thomas Bell and others took extremely ill we also held a Prayer Meeting at a Quarter to two When Tibbs.. Henry Sharp J Campbell Henry G Tyson William Palmer J Tibbs exhorted to us your H Sharp also.

THE TESTIMONY OF AN ENTOMBED MAN

Before Jim Amour the back-overman died, poisoned by the gas in the Hartley pit, he left a written message of which this is a facsimile. It tells of a prayer meeting which a few of the men had held at a quarter to two on Friday afternoon . . .

PHOTO-COPY BY J. C. CURRY

ROBERT TURNBULL

Robert Turnbull was a pitman from Cowpen who did noble work at the time of the disaster. Reid, the journalist, described him as "A tall, singular-looking man with long curling ringlets and a shaggy beard". Night and day he stayed at the Hartley pit-head. He presided at many of the mass meetings which took place there, and he announced to the waiting multitude the names of the dead as they were brought from the pit.

PHOTO-COPY BY J. C. CURRY

JAMES MATHER

James Mather of South Shields was a great campaigner on behalf of the miners. In the agitation which followed in the wake of the Hartley disaster, Mather was very much to the fore, exerting all his powers on their behalf.

PHOTO-COPY BY J. C. CURRY

Bethel, this tiny House of God, where the Methodists were wont with spirit and understanding to sing their hymns of praise, where fervent prayers found voice, telling of the trials of the faithful, of their temptations and their rejoicings in the glory of the Lord, where "Hallelujahs" rang out and "raised the roof"—here today it was all so different.

It was silent now. A House of Death. Here a ghostly company had moved in and had taken possession. Lying across the pews, cumbering up the aisle and in every open space, black coffins were disposed, all with unscrewed lids revealing haunting ghost-like faces. George Cooke's poem notes that:

> They lay unclaimed in that cold place,
> With pit clothes on and blackened face.

And anxious, sad-faced relatives gathered around, and peered intently at the contents of each coffin in turn, seeking therein some semblance of their own untraced and beloved breadwinner.

Now and then the identity of the pathetic remains in the coffin was established and the excitement of the bereaved was terrible. Recognition was registered with no language but a cry of anquish.

In general, however, there was an air of quiet here. And as the subdued searchers filed around the black coffins, treading lightly and speaking in murmurs, the only other sound was the swish of the voluminous Victorian garments which brushed lightly past the pews, or, in the similitude of soft whispers, gently swept the sides of the coffins.

The aspect of grief was visible on every face, and in this incongruous little sanctuary, the songs of praise were, for the time being, silent.

Meanwhile, Sunday though it was, exploration of the pit continued. Three men who are named for us as "Todd, Parker and Sheelie" went down the pit to try to force their way to the staple and down it if possible. When they came up again they reported that they had been right along the Yard Seam as far as the staple which they found had 18 feet of water in it, proving that the Low Main Seam was entirely flooded. No more bodies had been encountered in their search and they were satisfied that none remained in the pit.

Yet, since there were those who said there might still be bodies which had been overlooked, it was decided to make doubly sure. So Mr. Coulson himself, and a certain Mr. Cole described as "a pitman from Monkwearmouth who has been most energetic in the recovery of the bodies", went through the village to every house where a loss had been sustained in order to see if anyone was still missing. In furtherance of this matter others were delegated to go to more distant places, and so it was finally established that all had been accounted for in one way or another. Hence it was decided to stop all further work at the pit.

Ever since dawn a crowd had been building up in Hartley in readiness for the funeral. They streamed in on foot from all parts of the compass. They came in cabs, gigs, dog-carts and "traps" of every description. But chiefly they descended in "immense shoals" from the railway station. That little railway station had never known such activity in all its life. All the past week it had shown an astonishing capacity for unloading crowds of sightseers, but today, as train after train arrived, the local citizens could not believe their eyes at the spectacle of so great a press and throng.

Many of the visitors were miners from other collieries. Reid says he could tell these belonged to "the class of miners" because they were "attired in the showy garments which this class so much affects, velvet waistcoats and white feathers being very common articles of apparel!"

But despite this gaiety of dress the crowd was visibly impressed with the solemnity of the occasion. Not a few of the women were weeping bitterly, while the gloomy looks and suppressed voices of the men showed that they also were very much affected. It was a strange sight this great crowd, and one so alien to this quiet hard-working and normally obscure community. The side of the pit-heap nearest the railway station had assumed the appearance of a fair-ground or a race meeting. In one section there was parked a motley collection of horse-drawn vehicles which had brought in their passengers by road, and not far away stalls had been set up for the sale of "edibles and drinkables" chiefly tea, for which latter there was a great demand. Some people frowned on this commercial activity viewing it as an exploitation of an event which had brought tragedy to so many homes, but on the whole it was recognized as justified in the circumstances.

The correspondent of the **Illustrated London News** estimated that a crowd of 60,000 invaded Hartley on that funeral day. The visitors wandered curiously around the pit-heap, and gazed through the cottage doors with their eyes rivetted on the coffins. But the religious organisations saw their opportunity and were not slow to arrange pithead religious services.

The biggest of these was held in front of the platform from which announcements had been made during the abortive rescue operations. Amongst those taking part were the Rev. R. E. Mason, Incumbent, and the Rev. D. T. Jones, Curate, both of Earsdon; Rev. J. C. Bruce, LL.D., Newcastle; Messrs. J. H. Marshall, W. Furness, and J. B. Alexander. Mr. Charles Carr, Head Viewer of Hartley Colliery was also present. The service commenced with the hymn : "Before Jehovah's awful Throne."

Mr. Mason then read the following letter which had been received from Sir Charles B. Phipps, Secretary to Her Majesty the Queen :—

Osborne, January 23rd, 1862.

Sir,

The Queen, in the midst of her own overwhelming grief, has taken the deepest interest in the dreadful accident at Hartley, and, up to the last had hoped that at least a considerable number of the poor people might have been recovered. The appalling news since received has affected the Queen very much. Her Majesty commands me to say that her tenderest sympathy is with the poor widows and mothers, and that her own misery makes her feel the more for them. Her Majesty hopes that everything will be done, as far as possible, to alleviate their distress, and her Majesty will feel a sad satisfaction in assisting such measures. Pray let me know what is doing.

To Charles Carr, Esq.,   I have the honour to be, Sir,
Hartley Colliery,   Your Obedient Servant,
Newcastle-on-Tyne.   C. B. PHIPPS.

The references to the Queen's "own grief" concerned, of course, the recent death of the Prince Consort.

While this religious service was still in progress a number of people had to leave to prepare for their departure in funeral procession to Cramlington, where some nine or ten bodies were to be interred. It was necessary for them to get away before the big general funeral since Cramlington was more distant. Mr. Mason and Mr. Jones had also to get off to Earsdon to prepare for the big main burial there. The **Illustrated London News** tells us that a few separate burials took place at Cowpen and Seghill as well as those at Cramlington.

But, before describing the big funeral itself two items of interest are worthy of note. Both took place after the funeral processions had departed. One was the holding of a second great religious service at the pit-heap, promoted it seems, by Rev. Dr. Bruce of Newcastle.

Thousands attended this service and listened attentively to the prayers, scripture readings and addresses and, above all, to the singing of the hymns which so many voices rendered with great spirit and feeling. The sense of tragedy all about these people might not have put a new song in their mouths, but it certainly put a new zest and earnestness into their singing. How impressive and moving must this occasion have been, seen against the gaunt background of the pit-head!

The other event was altogether different. It likewise took place after the funerals had left Hartley. It may sound some-what strange to us today, but considering all the circumstances there was much to be said for it. The event can be summed up in the phrase "Sixpence to see the Pitheap!"

And that is just what happened. Great crowds were wandering aimlessly about, idly curious of this and that at Hartley Colliery when Robert Turnbull had a brain-wave. Why not turn this to good account to assist the relief fund! So, as Reid tells us:

> Suddenly Mr. Turnbull came forward to the edge of the platform and announced that, as all operations in the shaft were now sus-pended, and as a great desire was felt to view the scene of the late

calamity it had been resolved to admit the general public to view the shaft and buildings upon payment of sixpence each, the money received going, of course, to the fund for the relief of the sufferers.

Hence, in a very short time the pit buildings were swarming with people. They crowded into the engine house, they peered into the black depths of the fatal shaft whilst they listened with the deepest interest to any account however preposterous given by anybody who professed to have some knowledge of the accident and its causes. Many even climbed to the top of the engine house the better to inspect from that position the appearance of the remaining half of the broken beam.

Reid seems to suggest that there was something not quite right about this show business. True, it helped the relief fund, for on that first Sunday afternoon it produced £30. But there's a hint of disapproval in his comment :

> Very different did the place appear then from what it appeared during the dreadfully cold and stormy nights at the beginning of the week, when a few half-starved men, sustained only by the noble desire of saving life, were the sole possessors of the platform. It was strange now to see dainty ladies and dandy youths standing upon the place where so recently a great battle between life and death had been fought out, standing too upon the very spot where yesterday a scene was taking place (the raising of the bodies) which would have thrilled the blood in their veins and sickened their very hearts.

But the great event of that sad Sunday was the big burial of the victims of the Hartley disaster.

First there was the small contingent which set off for Cramlington. The nine or ten coffins were brought out of the cottages concerned, placed in two or three common country carts, and covered with white cloths. The carts, followed by a few mourners and a large number of spectators then set off in slow procession to Cramlington.

Earlier in this book the Hartley disaster was described as an event unparalleled in mining history. So too was that funeral procession from Hartley to the churchyard at Earsdon.

Simonin, the French writer on mining, refers to Hartley in his **Mines and Miners** (1868) and says of the funeral, "Was ever a larger or more mournful procession beheld in time of war or pestilence?" And Fynes feels the scene too poignant for words when he says :

> It is idle to write of the grief which prevailed, for no writer can adequately describe the universal mourning which took possession of the whole community. The mournful procession from Hartley to Earsdon where they were buried presented an appearance indescribably agonizing.

Conscious, as one must be, of the limitations referred to by Fynes adequately to describe the great event of that day, it is nevertheless possible from contemporary accounts, chiefly Reid's to follow the performance of those last sad rites.

Between twelve noon and one o'clock a convoy of common country carts, each containing a layer of straw in the bottom, pulled into the muddy street of Hartley village. A cart stopped at almost every cottage. In one or two cases, instead of the rough common country cart, a one-horse hearse was to be seen.

Friends and relations had in the meantime gathered in their best Sunday black, at the cottage doors of the bereaved to pay their last respects. Ere long the sound of singing "rough but not unmelodious" was heard coming from within some of the houses. This singing took place chiefly in the houses of those connected with the Primitive Methodist chapel. These brethren held a short service in each house, consisting of a prayer and the singing of a hymn. The hymn most favoured was well known to them and commenced : "Thee we adore, Eternal Name . . . "

But, says Reid, rough, rude and simple as it was, there was connected with it a strong and manly energy well suited to the occasion.

The report in the **Illustrated London News** tells us that the hymn "O God our help in Ages Past" was "sung in mournful cadence and, with the wailing of the widows and the sobs of the orphan children, the effect was almost overpowering."

The **Times** notes that in these circumstances the ministrations of the womenfolk from near and far were a real blessing—

> The street of the village is filled with the women who steal noiselessly from house to house on their mission of mercy endeavouring

by arts only known to women to impart solace to these bereaved ones. Truly they are the very realisation of the poet's fancy . . .

When pain and sickness wring the brow
A ministering angel thou.

At last, in one cottage after another, the sound of the singing ceased. Another work, that of screwing down the lids of the coffins was commenced. The coffins were then brought forth and placed upon the uncouth hearses. In some of the carts there was only one coffin, in others there were more. The saddest sight of all was, of course, that of the Liddle's which contained seven coffins. Generally a white cloth was thrown over the black deal coffin, on the lid of which the dead man's name still remained written in chalk.

One after another the horses, urged forward by a word of command and a gentle flick of a whip, tightened in the shafts and pulled slowly down the road. Each cart had its own especial contingent of mourners, who mutely plodded in the rear. Even Reid's ready pen seems to falter when he says "It is impossible to describe the effect produced by this strange procession of death."

Looking from the cottages, as far as the eye could reach, on the road leading to the quiet little church at Earsdon, a mingled crowd of spectators, mourners and carts covered with huge white sheets was all that could be seen. Not less than fifty of these carts were at one moment making their way towards the churchyard. And they contained, the reporter tells us, "The bodies of some of the finest men who ever descended a pit, men who would have done honour to any station in life." Then the writer continues, "There was something dreadful in thinking of the desolation which the departing carts left behind them. That which had been a misfortune to the kingdom generally, has been the destruction of the village of New Hartley."

The procession of death moved on. Earsdon lay about four miles from New Hartley and the first rough hearse had arrived at the church before the last one had left the colliery. There was scarcely a break in the procession throughout the whole of that distance.

As already indicated, the burial ground attached to the parish church at Earsdon was totally inadequate to the needs of the present occasion. After all it was less than two years since the bodies of many of the miners lost in the nearby Burradon Pit Explosion (which cost 75 lives) were brought to this same churchyard. Such a mortality rate was far beyond the normal expectations of the parish. So now a gap was made in the old churchyard wall and access thereby made to an adjoining field. There the virgin land was measured up and gouged out to the requirements of the different graves. Arranged in three rows some few graves were made to take a single coffin; others were designed for two, three, four and more. One immense trench was made to contain no less than thirty-three bodies, this being chiefly for the unknown dead.

The gravediggers had indeed a gruelling task; the labour entailed in digging these numerous and enormous graves was arduous in the extreme. Nearly fifty men were employed nonstop from before dawn on the Saturday until after dark on the Sunday evening of the funeral. One can imagine the grim scene of the diggers working by the light of lanterns in those dark hours of mid winter !

The excavations covered one acre of ground, and in some places the work was especially hard for solid rock to a depth of six feet had to be cut into. Well used, as many of these men were, to hard labour, how many blistered hands and aching bodies must there not have been ere this task was completed ? Moreover, for these toilers it was a race against time, for a great many of the bodies had already been interred before the last trenches were got ready for the reception of the remainder. At one time it looked as though the coffins were queuing up awaiting their turn for burial. About 180 were buried here. Some few found a last resting place in spaces reserved for them in the old churchyard beside forbears who had loved and watched over them in their infancy.

Those in charge of this prodigious burial business also worked under very great pressure. The Rev. R. E. Mason, Incumbent of Earsdon, Rev. D. T. Jones, Curate of the same parish, Rev. E. Carr of London (brother of the owners of Hartley Colliery), Rev. Hugh Taylor formerly of Shilbottle —all applied themselves to the proper and reverent discharge of their functions despite the wholesale nature of the task of burial.

Mention must be made of the great responsibility suddenly thrust upon the shoulders of Mr. John Edwards, one of the churchwardens of Earsdon; to plan and supervise the lay-out and the digging of the graves and trenches.

When the carts containing the coffins arrived at Earsdon, they were drawn up in rows until the last had arrived.

Then the Rev. R. E. Mason led the burial service . . .

> I am the resurrection and the life : he that believeth in me though he were dead, yet shall he live : and whosoever liveth and believeth in me shall never die.

While the words of the burial service were being said, pick-axes could still be heard hurriedly pounding the earth in the preparation of the last of the graves.

And one by one the coffins were lowered into the graves.

Reid gives us a vivid picture of his standing there amidst the graves. He describes the feeling of awe which possessed him when, with darkness descending, coffins lay all about him awaiting burial :

> When the solemn words, 'Ashes to ashes and dust to dust' were being uttered, darkness had well-nigh fallen upon the awful scene. And the indescribable feeling of awe which the thought of being in the midst of so many unburied human remains occasioned, and from which the spectator was separated by a few feet of space and a few thin deal boards, was intensified by the falling gloom of the evening.

It was a strange graveyard this, he comments, more like the scene of slaughter of a battlefield than that of the slain in peaceful industry. And so it was.

It was an unforgettable day, this, as the blanket of the dark descended upon the Earsdon graveyard.

Unforgettable the cold raw night with its sighing wind, the gravediggers still toiling by the light of lanterns, the clods of earth thumping down on the coffins; the sad, shadowy, spectral figures of the bereaved moving slowly about the mounds of earth, the tower of the church seen dimly in the background, the grievous sound somewhere in the darkness of women sobbing, the whole black, dismal despair of this unhappy, austere night . . .

No star shone in the winter sky that night as the mourners sad of heart and heavy laden, homeward turned their weary way, back to Hartley, and what was left of home.

PART FOUR

The Death Blow to the One-Shaft System

Chapter 1

THE CORONER'S INQUEST

While the fight for the lives of the 199 men and boys still in the pit was at its height, the inquest on the five men killed in the shaft was opened at Seaton Delaval, not far from Hartley.

This took place at the Hastings Arms Inn there, before Stephen Reed, Esq., coroner. Amongst those present was Mr. Matthias Dunn, the Government Inspector of Mines for Northumberland. A short report of the inquest appears in the Newcastle Courant for 24th June, 1862. This inquest was, of course, but a curtain-raiser to the main inquiry which was held after the rest of the bodies had been brought out of the pit, and which lasted four days.

The reader, aware of the great drama which was enacted in the shaft mentioned earlier in this book, and which concerned Thomas Watson and his friends, might think that the cold official language of the verdict was quite inadequate to the occasion. But it was, of course, a formality pending the fuller investigation which was to come two weeks later.

The verdict at this first inquest session was as follows :

That Robert Bewick was accidentally killed in the shaft of the New Hartley Pit by the breaking of the engine beam and the falling of the same into the pit shaft.

The press report quoting this concludes with the words, "A similar verdict was returned in respect of the other four men and the proceedings terminated." Just a handful of toilers trapped in the shaft following the breaking of the beam, half of which crashed down and smashed the cage in which they were riding to bank. But how much more of human interest that episode contained to uplift and inspire, the reader already knows.

The main inquest on the 199 who had been entombed in the pit, was opened on Monday, 3rd February, 1862, at the United

Methodist Free Chapel, Seaton Delaval. The coroner was again Mr. Stephen Reed, and the jury the same as that on the previous occasion.

It is impossible within the scope of this book to cover the whole detailed proceedings which were spread over four days, reports of which occupied many columns in the local newspapers. So I propose to confine myself to a few references to the evidence given there and to quote more fully later the important report which Mr. J. Kenyon Blackwell submitted to the Home Secretary. Mr. Blackwell had been specially sent down by the Home Office to assist the coroner at the inquest; and, since there was so much public interest and concern, detailed terms of reference were set out in a document for his guidance.

Press reports mention as being present at the inquest, in addition to Mr. Blackwell, Mr. Matthias Dunn, Mr. T. E. Forster and Mr. G. B. Forster both mining engineers, Mr. T. C. Maynard, coroner for the Easington Ward of Durham, Mr. G. W. Cram, and Joseph Cowan, Junior, of Blaydon.

Amongst the first to be called to give evidence was our friend Thomas Watson, who described something of his ordeal in the shaft. William Coulson, master sinker, told of what he found on first going down the shaft on the Friday (the day following the disaster) the broken timbers, the falling stone, and the extreme danger of it all. Then there was the sudden discharge of gas on the following Tuesday, which caused several of his men to be brought to bank speechless, his own son among them. His men were using common candles and the effect of the gas was to make them burn brighter.

Coulson described how he himself went down into the gas and on his return had a consultation with other mining engineers, the outcome of which was the decision to instal the canvas brattice. "Emmerson, one of my men" he said, "went down the pit on Wednesday after the brattice was put in and was brought to bank very ill." Then he spoke of the ugly mood of the crowd and of how he advised the management to let one or two of their number go down to see for themselves the state of things. Details of Mr. Coulson's own great experience in pit-sinking, already referred to, were brought out by questions from Mr. Blackwell.

Mr. John Short, enginewright of the colliery, gave information about the pumping engine. It was, he said, of 300 H.P. The beam, made by Losh, Wilson and Bell, weighed 42 tons and was made of cast-iron. He spoke of the rescue of the men trapped in the shaft and the recovery of the cages late on the night of the disaster.

Mr. Joseph Humble, the "Resident-Viewer" or colliery manager in the course of his evidence gave the output of Hartley Colliery as 350 tons per day. There were 43 ponies in the pit. Candles were in common use but in his exploration of the workings after the disaster he took a Davy lamp "on the suggestion of Mr. Dunn the Inspector."

He spoke of seeing the bodies in the pit. Adams and Wilson (a third man was named later as Robert Boyd) were the first to discover them. But when he (Humble) saw them below ground they were lying so close to each other that he "had to step on them to get over them."

William Adams, whom we have already met in our story as the first man to enter the death pit, said he lived at Cowpen, was a miner, and went to Hartley as a volunteer rescue worker :

> Robert Wilson of New Backworth was with me and about 4 o'clock on the afternoon of Wednesday, 22nd January, we went down the shaft into the furnace drift and found two men lying on top of the furnace bars. We continued and found more bodies. I believe I saw about a hundred. The hole by which we got into the furnace drift was about three feet square.

John Taylor was next to be called. He described himself as "A coal owner and viewer." He was, he said, "the check-viewer" on behalf of the ground landlord, Lord Hastings. He had requested Mr. Coulson to "superintend the ridding (clearing) of the shaft." He gave evidence concerning the attitude of the crowd at the pit who were "complaining very much of the slow progress of the work." After consultation between Coulson and himself, it was agreed to let representatives of the men go down the pit to see for themselves. Hence Adams and Wilson went down.

William K. Horsley, engine builder of Seaton Sluice, spoke of erecting the pumping engine at Hartley in 1855.

One fact of importance which was brought out in the cross examination of Mr. Humble, the resident viewer, was that the sump of the shaft had never been cleaned out. The comment was later made that such neglect could have led to a clogging of the pump-buckets with a resulting strain on the spears or connecting rods and in turn on the beam of the engine.

Mr. Blackwell asked questions as to what it would have cost to put in a staple between the High Main and the Yard Seam—that vital missing link which would have enabled the men to escape from the pit.

Mr. Humble, could not answer that, so Mr. Coulson was recalled.

> **Blackwell :** What would have been the cost of a five foot staple from the High Main to the Yard Seam?
> **Coulson :** £300 at the outside.

Our natural comment today might well be, "Oh that that £300 had been spent whereby 204 precious lives would have been saved !"

Coulson went on to say that it would have taken fifteen weeks to make the staple.

He was then asked what it actually cost him to sink the Hartley Pit from bank to sump :

> **Coulson :** The Hartley Pit, the present pit, cost £3,600 to begin with.
> **Coroner :** The pit shaft?
> **Coulson :** Yes, the Hartley pit, one hundred fathoms to the sump.

Thus, step by step, the sad story of the disaster was re-enacted ere the inquest drew to its close. There were technical questions for the mining engineer like those addressed to Mr. Coulson. There were questions about the running of the pit like those put to Mr. Humble. There were simple factual questions like those put to Thomas Watson about his experiences when trapped in the shaft.

Then came one dramatic moment when a witness told of how he found a message which had been written by one of the

Dr. ANTHONY DAVISON,
M.R.C.S.E.

Dr. Davison, the Colliery Surgeon at Hartley, was in charge of the team of doctors who were available for service at Hartley during those disaster days.

Dr. Davison was at the pit-head at all hours. He attended to the sinkers, and examined the bodies recovered from the pit. See his letter to the **Lancet** quoted in an appendix to this book.

PHOTO-COPY BY J. C. CURRY

Dr. GILBERT WARD,
M.R.C.S.

Dr. Ward of Blyth was also in attendance at the Hartley pit. He too rendered aid to the sinkers, and stood by for long periods awaiting the recovery of the entombed men.

PHOTO-COPY BY J. C. CURRY

THE HARTLEY DISASTER MEDAL

The deep sense of appreciation of the noble work of the sinkers who risked their lives in the attempted rescue work at Hartley, took the form of grants of medals and money.

Mr. Wyon of the Mint designed the medal. The medals were struck in silver with the exception of that for Mr. Coulson, which was in gold.

entombed men. The witness was Mr. W. R. Cole, the viewer
from Bebside. He said that in the course of his exploration of
the Yard Seam he came across the body of Jim Amour, the
back-overman. One can imagine the breathless interest which
would be displayed in the hushed courtroom, as Cole described
how he took from the dead man's pocket his overman's report
book. He had flicked over the pages and fixed upon one particular entry. It had nothing to do with the presence of gas or
the general state of the pit. It spoke of a prayer meeting. A
prayer meeting in that pit of death in which a number of men
had taken part. There it was on record . . . And reproduced
in this book for all to see.

On the fourth day of the inquest the verdict was given. It
is quoted here in full from Home Office documents and is as
follows :

HARTLEY COLLIERY ACCIDENT.

Verdict of the Jury at the Inquest held on **John Galligher,*** the sixth
day of February, 1862.

We, the Coroner and Jury, do find, that the said John Galligher,
on the twenty-second day of January last, was found dead in the
workings of New Hartley Colliery, having died therein from the
inhalation of gas, being shut up in the yard seam of the said Colliery, on the sixteenth day of the said month, when the shaft was
closed by the accidental breaking of the engine beam, which, with
other materials, fell into the working shaft of the pit, and there
being no exit therefrom, all access to the deceased was cut off, and
he perished from the cause above-mentioned. The Jury cannot
close this painful inquiry without expressing their strong opinion
of the imperative necessity that all working collieries should have
at least a second shaft or outlet, to afford the workmen the means
of escape, should any obstruction take place, as occurred at the
New Hartley Pit; and that in future, the beams of colliery engines
should be made of malleable iron, instead of cast metal. They also
take occasion to notice with admiration the heroic courage of the
viewers and others, who, at the risk of their own lives, for so many
nights and days devoted their best skill and energy to rescue the
unfortunate men who were lost, and that everything which human
agency could accomplish was done towards that humane object.

I certify the above to be a true copy.

(signed) **Stephen Reed,** Coroner. (Seal).

* "Galligher" is the spelling on the Home Office document; "Gallagher" on local
Memorial, etc.

Chapter 2

THE REACTIONS OF THE PRESS AND THE PUBLIC

Apart from the coroner's inquest, it was inevitable that so tragic an event should give rise to much discussion and many other "inquests". Wherever men foregathered Hartley was the topic of conversation, and these talks had common ground in the desire to learn lessons from the disaster.

But the debates differed in their sense of nearness to the danger and consequently in the degree of warmth with which the lessons were driven home. To the miners themselves this was a desperate life and death matter which brooked no further delay.

I propose in the present section of this book to view this concern about the lessons of Hartley from the different points of view—the reactions of the press and the public; the reports of the Government Inspectors and the debates of the mining engineers; the campaign of the miners themselves; and the ultimate compulsion of all this on the Legislature.

Take first the **Comment in the Press.** The newspapers in general underlined the lessons. The **Illustrated London News** (1.2.1862), said that one very obvious method of diminishing the risk to the miners' lives was "the provision of duplicate means of entry and exit" to every pit. It cannot be pretended, the report said, that the catastrophe at the Hartley Pit was needed to suggest this common sense precaution. Pitmen had for a long time agitated for the adoption of this indispensable pre-requisite for their security and. . .

> What the dictates of common sense and the suggestions of humanity have hitherto failed to enforce, the recent calamity, no doubt, will be the means of obtaining.

Even before the Hartley bodies were brought out of the pit the **Newcastle Courant** (24.1.1862) was quickly forthcoming in its strictures. Its criticism went beyond the absence of a second shaft. Why was the beam which broke made of cast-iron instead of wrought iron ? Why wasn't there a staple connecting the Yard Seam with the High Main Seam ?

> It is not for us but for more competent individuals and legally constituted tribunals to pronounce a judgement how far censure (if any) attaches to individuals for dereliction of duty in connection with the working of the colliery. But this brief word we will not refrain from adding. Had the fatal beam been made of wrought iron instead of cast iron, had there been two shafts at the colliery instead of one, or had the air staple by which the miners ascended from the Low Main to the Yard Seam been continued to the High Main above, the lives of the men and boys in the pit might have been saved. Had any one of these precautions been taken—any, or all of them, being quite practicable— this melancholy catastrophe might never have occurred. Simple in its cause, yet terrible in its consequences, the accident teaches us with a fearful emphasis, some equally simple lessons of precaution as to the future.

The greatest voice of all, in the world of the press was that of the **Times.** From time to time in this book I quote the authoritative comment of that newspaper. Here is one typical quotation (following some pronouncements on the disaster) which reveals the paper's sense of purpose and responsibility "It is a necessity of our calling to extract these cautions for the future; it is a duty with us to find in this frightful disaster some warning against its recurrence". And it saw the issue clearly as the following conclusion shows :—

> Surely no reason can be alleged except the trifling one of expense against a second shaft sufficient for the escape of the men if need be. How so obvious a precaution came to be overlooked we know not. The expedient of a second shaft is so obvious that very good reason indeed must be shown against it if its absence is to be further tolerated.

In addition to the constructive comment in the press there was the unqualified **Support of the General Public.**

As Fynes rightly said : "This accident excited more inquiry into the nature of the work of the miners than any previous casualty had done". Indeed the conscience of the nation, so long indifferent as to what was happening in the dark satanic mines of the country, was at last awakened and interested.

The measure of this concern was reflected in the monetary contributions which were truly amazing. They came in from rich and poor, from far and near. Queen Victoria sent £200, the Duke of Northumberland £300, the Earl of Durham £200 and a collection on the London Stock Exchange raised £500.

Matthias Dunn reported on this generosity as follows :—

> The calamity brought about the most extraordinary public feeling for the families of the sufferers, contributions being brought in from all parts of the kingdom to the tune of upwards of £80,000, which has so far exceeded all reasonable requirements as to demand Parliamentary interference to make an ultimate settlement of the funds.

Queen Victoria not only contributed money to the Relief Fund, but she also sent a personal letter to the bereaved. This gesture aroused great interest in the country and a well-known artist made it the subject of a painting. The great preacher, Charles Haddon Spurgeon, in his characteristic way, described Her Majesty as "The Empress of Sorrow" in thus comforting the mourners.

Then there was the work of the poets. One of these works made particular reference to the Queen's act in thus writing to the bereaved. The poem was entitled **The Queen has sent a Letter** written by Edward Corvan soon after the disaster. Here are a few lines taken at random from the poem :

> Oh bless the Queen of England who sympathy doth show
> Towards our stricken widows amid their grief and woe
> To send a letter stating "I share your sorrows here"
> To soothe the aching hearts of all and dry the widow's tear.
>
> .   .   .   .
>
> Show me the page in history where deeds heroic shine
> More bright than our Northumbrian men the heroes of the mine.
> God speed the hardy collier and Coulson's gallant band
> Who braved the perils of the shaft with willing heart and hand
> For the Queen has sent a letter though she mourns a husband dear
> To soothe the aching hearts of all and dry the widow's tear.

Joseph Skipsey, described as a "Pitman's Poet" of his day, wrote a long poem entitled **The Hartley Calamity** which he often rendered with great dramatic effect to various audiences

in his money-raising efforts for the benefit of the Relief Fund.
It begins :

> The Hartley men are noble, and
>   Ye'll hear a tale of woe ;
> I'll tell the doom of the Hartley men
>   The year of sixty-two.

He proceeds to describe the pit's normal workaday life going
on underground before the disaster . . .

> On, on they toil, with heat they broil,
>   And the streams of sweat still glue
> The stour into their skins till they
>   Are as black as the coal they hew.

He next tells of the breaking of the beam and of the vigil at
the pit, culminating in the final "sleep" of the entombed :

> And fathers and mothers, and sisters and brothers
>   The lover and the new-made bride—
> A vigil kept for those who slept
>   From eve to morning tide.

> But they slept—still sleep—in silence dread
>   Two hundred old and young
> To awake when heaven and earth have sped
>   And the last dread trumpet rung.

But perhaps George Cooke's poem also entitled **The Hartley
Calamity,** is the most purposive of all, because it points the
moral of the Hartley affair. It sums up the strong public feeling
of the period concerning the evil of the one-shaft system. The
following lines are culled from the poem :

> Ten score lives have proved it true
> The one-shaft system will not do
> The horrid system one way out
> Has slain its hundreds there's no doubt
> May Hartley in the memory live,
> A death-blow to the system give

And Hartley did indeed achieve that undying fame.

117

Chapter 3

THE REPORTS OF
H.M. GOVERNMENT INSPECTORS AND THE DEBATE
OF THE MINING ENGINEERS.

There are in existence two official reports from Government Officers on the Hartley Disaster, one from Mr. Dunn the Inspector of Mines for the area, and the other from the specially appointed Inspector who attended the inquest at the request of the Home Secretary :—

(1)—THE REPORT OF MATTHIAS DUNN

Mr. Dunn was the Government's Inspector of Mines for the area. It is important here, in view of the criticism later directed against him, for the reader to have some idea of the extensive region for which Mr. Dunn was responsible. He had the oversight of the Northern District which comprised the Counties of Durham, Northumberland and Cumberland.

Dunn's Report for the year ending 31st December, 1862, makes very sad reading. It also contains an interesting reference to certain apprehensions felt by the miners at Hartley in the months before the disaster. They had called upon Mr. Dunn's services because of their concern about certain matters affecting the safety of the pit.

But let us first glance at his general review of the year 1862. He described it as "exceedingly lamentable." This was particularly so since it followed closely upon the heavy losses of life in the previous year. In that year there had occurred, in addition to the many individual fatal casualties in the pits, the loss of 75 lives by an explosion at Burradon (under the same coalowners as Hartley) and 22 lives at Hetton.

And then Mr. Dunn graphically relates the story of the alarm felt by the miners at Hartley about the danger of the pit being flooded. A broken beam and a blocked shaft were never thought of. It was flooding which was dreaded.

Their workings were surrounded by water which was held back by a barrier of coal of unknown thickness. In the day to day working of the pit test holes were drilled through this barrier in advance of the actual working of the coal. What the men feared was that these waters would break through the coal, bringing the added danger of gas from the "waste" and, with only one exit at the shaft, they would then be trapped like rats. Hence, only six months before the disaster occurred, the men of Hartley "demanded" intervention by the Inspector. Here is Mr. Dunn's Report:

In the month of July, 1861, the men of this colliery addressed to me a letter demanding my attention to the mode of boring against the surrounding water, to which I immediately responded by examining the process which was extensively practised to ascertain the exact position of the neighbouring drowned waste.

After doing which along with a deputation of the workmen, I directed my attention to a staple pit which had already been sunk between the Yard Coal Seam and the Low Main below (14 fathoms) which was judged as a great safeguard against any unexpected flow of water, the shaft bottom being some fathoms below the level of this staple.

Seeing that the staple was without any means of ascent from the Low Main to the Yard Coal, I addressed a letter to the owners and the men of the colliery of which the following is an extract:

Newcastle-on-Tyne,
July 23rd, 1861.

As a safeguard against the danger of a heavy discharge of water I think it imperative that an effectual and convenient ladder (long since arranged for) should be completed without delay at the Yard Coal Staple as a means of escape for the people.

These suggestions were without delay carried out, and therefore when the catastrophe occurred, it afforded great satisfaction for me to think that at any rate the people could all ascend out of the reach of the water and of the ruined shaft between the two seams.

Dunn then refers to the gas which killed the entombed men. It was presumed to have been carbonic oxide gas generated by the dying embers of the furnace in the Yard Seam, together with the diminished ventilation which allowed the gases of the mine to accumulate.

It was inevitable that Dunn's Report should make reference to the great outcry about the need for two shafts. And he goes on : "In consequence of this calamity much discussion in the public papers and otherwise has taken place as to the propriety of every colliery having at least two shafts or outlets for the people in cases of explosion, inundation, etc., and these discussions have brought about an amended law upon the subject dated 7th August, 1862."

*   *   *

(2)—THE REPORT OF J. KENYON BLACKWELL

Mr. Blackwell was the Government Inspector of Mines for the Midland District. He attended the inquest in compliance with a request made by the Home Secretary on the suggestion of Mr. Dunn.

It is indicative of the seriousness with which the Home Secretary viewed this enquiry (in view of the great public concern) that specific documentary guidance was given to Mr. Blackwell as to the nature of the task committed to him.

This document from the Home Office said that Mr. Dunn had felt that "some person free from any local influence" should assist the coroner and jury, and, in view of his great practical experience it gave the Home Secretary much satisfaction that he (Mr. Blackwell) had agreed to attend the inquest. You will carefully watch the evidence, he was told, and put such questions as you think important.

> That the inquiry should be a searching one, is not only due to the feelings of the large body of persons immediately affected by this melancholy event, and to the universal sympathy with them which has been so strongly evinced, but it is demanded by the still higher consideration of the duty of ascertaining what precautions can and ought to be taken in order to guard as far as possible against the recurrence of such a lamentable loss of life.
>
> **—Home Office Papers.**

Mr. Blackwell was told to report as to the safety or otherwise of the use of heavy cast-iron beams. Furthermore there were two matters to which his attention was especially directed, (1) the condition of the shaft—were the sides securely supported, etc. ? and, (2) "most important"—the practicability of enforcing a general regulation that communication with the surface should be provided by more than a single shaft." The careful wording of this document shows urgency and concern and its despatch to Blackwell was more than a mere departmental formality.

Mr. Blackwell attended the inquest and played his part in making it a "searching one." His report is given in full in an appendix to this book so it will suffice to make brief reference to it here.

The lives lost, he reports, totalled 204, 5 in the shaft and 199 in the pit, together with 43 pit ponies.

The shaft of the Hartley Pit had not been walled except for a short distance from the surface. Below that the weak parts of the shaft had been lined with wooden planks.

The quantity of water at the pit was very large, 1400 to 1500 gallons per minute, which was lifted 200 yards to the surface and required great engine power. There was a tract of old drowned workings in the Low Main Seam in the Hartley Royalty connected with a pit called the Mill Pit, and before the accident an exploring drift from the Hartley Pit workings was being carried towards this drowned tract preceded by bore holes. These holes had tapped the water and it was running from the old workings into the Hartley Pit at the time of the accident.

The Inspector of Mines for the district (Mr. Dunn) "recognising the danger to be apprehended at the Hartley Pit from a possible sudden influx of water, and for the improvement of the ventilation of the pit", had induced the owners to sink the staple from the Yard Seam to the Low Main.

The Inspector had also procured the placing of a ladder in this staple, by means of which, after the accident, all the men escaped to the Yard Seam. Unfortunately, there was no communication above this to the surface except that via the shaft itself, which was blocked.

Then Inspector Blackwell goes into great detail about the pumping arrangements. One interesting fact seems to have been the tremendous weight of 55 tons hanging on the pit-shaft end of the beam which broke ! This was made up of dry and wet spears, buckets and columns of water in the bottom and middle sets of the pumps. As to the type of pumping engine in use, Mr. Blackwell found that there were weaknesses which were "a source of much danger." Then, too, it was proved that the sump at the bottom of the shaft had not been cleaned out for a great length of time. The timber of which the spears (or lifting rods) of the pumps in the shaft were made, was probably rendered brittle by the heat from the furnace in the upcast shaft. That the pumping engine was liable to breakage was proved by a former accident in 1858. On that occasion the main spear in the shaft broke. The engine-beam, the breakage of which was the immediate cause of the loss of life in the present accident was made of iron of only "fair quality." What actually caused the beam to break? It was due, said Mr. Blackwell, to the violent concussion to which it was subject after the counterbalancing load in the shaft had been lost through breakage there.

The sides of the shaft were not well secured. The timber which lined the weakest parts of the shaft to retain the strata, did not prevent them falling in to a considerable extent after the accident. The principal fall took place 30 feet above the Yard Seam where the sides of the shaft gave way to an extent 30 feet wide.

It seems to the present writer a great pity that the closing sentences of Blackwell's excellent report should introduce an element of equivocation. On the one hand he makes the categorical assertion that "It is indisputable that the working of mines of any description through a single shaft, introduces an element of **serious additional danger** into such operations"; Yet, pits, now in operation, he adds, might be forced to close down if they were to be compelled by law to provide a second shaft!

He is in no doubt about new pits—they should be made to have two shafts. As he rightly says:

> The evils and dangers arising from the use of single shafts in mining operations have, however, been already so fully acknowledged, and have been rendered so evident by this recent accident, that it appears desirable that such a system should not in future be permitted.

Nevertheless, with regard to the mines already in existence, caution was necessary. Despite the "serious additional danger" to which he refers, he felt it a difficult matter to arrive at "a just conclusion." Legislative enactment enforcing such additional outlay might close a lot of the pits then in operation!

(3)—THE DEBATE OF THE MINING ENGINEERS

It is to the credit of the North of England Institute of Mining Engineers that in the months following the Hartley Disaster, it conducted its own "inquest" in order to learn what it could from the tragedy.

In its official **Transactions** for the year 1862-63 we find this pointer almost on the first page "Discussions during the past year have been of peculiar interest, more especially those which arose out of the singularly unfortunate accident at Hartley Colliery."

At a meeting of the Institute on 6th March, 1862, a paper entitled "On the Accident at New Hartley Colliery" was given by George Baker Forster, M.A.—the paper which was summarised in an earlier chapter of this book.

This was followed on 4th October of that year by a full discussion of Mr. Forster's paper, the report of which occupies several pages in the Institute's **Transactions.**

Mr. Nicholas Wood, President of the Institute was in the chair, and he opened the debate by saying that the nature of the accident itself was unprecedented. He had been fifty years in the coal trade and during that time no accident of a similar nature had occurred. There were some features connected with the case which were worthy of attention so as to obviate similar accidents in future. The disaster had brought about a legislative enactment by which it was required that every mine should have two shafts or two means of egress from the workings of the colliery to the surface. The coalowners universally took up the question in a proper spirit and were determined to have two shafts to every mine although previously single shafts had to a considerable extent been used.

Mr. T. Y. Hall intervened to say that it was generally thought before the accident happened that the coalowners in the North of England considered two shafts were desirable, and nearly all those who had only one, were persevering to have two shafts.

The President said he did not want to contradict Mr. Hall but he never heard of that being agitated till this accident occurred.

Mr. G. B. Forster said that in this particular instance they were attempting to make a holing into the Old Mill Pit at Hartley and that would have been equivalent to a double shaft.

Mr. T. Y. Hall said that there was not one in ten of the shipping collieries of this district that had not a double shaft.

The President said he did not recollect the proportion of single to double shafts, but every one must have considered that two shafts were safer than one.

It might be noted here in passing that on this question of the proportion of single to double shafts the miners themselves in their agitation which followed in the wake of Hartley, sent deputations around the northern pits to ascertain the true position of things. Detailed returns of these tours are given in Fynes **History.** But, perhaps one might accept the short answer of Coulson to a question put to him at the Hartley Inquest as a fair sample of the general position :

> **Mr. Blackwell :** What proportion of the numerous winnings you have made, have been made with single shafts?
>
> **Mr. Coulson :** A great number, sir. I could not enumerate them exactly but I fancy something like 20 out of 84.

But to return once more to the debate of the mining engineers. The President said that taking the disaster as "a concatenation of several incidents" they should proceed to analyse these one by one. And this they did—whether the beam should have been made of wrought iron instead of cast iron; whether the beam should have been allowed to remain suspended over the pit shaft in the way it was without some "keps" device to prevent its fall down the shaft if it broke, etc. There was general agreement as to what caused the beam to break and that was that it was due to the breaking of one or two spears in the shaft. Next they considered the nature of the gas which killed the men in the pit. It could not they said, have been carbonic acid for the lights burned brighter; it could not have been carburetted hydrogen or the pit would have "fired". Hence they said it must have been carbonic oxide gas.

There was one aspect of the state of things at Hartley concerning which Mr. Nicholas Wood, the President of the Institute, did not mince his words. That was the unsafe manner in which the sides of the shaft had been lined. He reminded members of the Act of Parliament which prescribed that all shafts should be properly secured, and went on . . .

> If the sides of this shaft had been properly secured and walled, a great many of the evil effects would probably not have happened. **And certainly the timbering in this shaft could not be said to constitute proper security.** All shafts ought to be either walled with stone or with fire bricks.

At Hartley, said Mr. Wood, the timber holding the shaft sides had been torn away by the falling beam, and the resultant collapse of the earth and rubbish had sealed the pit. Had there been but a partial circulation of air up and down the shaft the men could have been saved . . .

> The only remedy is to have two shafts, and that may be presumed to be the perfect remedy.

Chapter 4

THE CAMPAIGN OF THE MINERS

Of all the agencies actively concerned on behalf of the miners, none, naturally, was so effective, and at times so vehement in its propaganda, as the miners themselves when they acted together.

There was still no enduring trade union amongst the miners. True, there had been loose, fitful organisations in which the counties of Durham and Northumberland had been associated for the fifty years preceding Hartley.

It was in the 1860's that the foundations of solid organisation were laid in the two counties, first jointly and then separately. The first step was that taken on Good Friday, 1863, (the year after Hartley) when the "Northumberland and Durham Miners' Mutual Confident Association" was formed. The two counties were, however, soon to go their separate ways, but the fact remains that union organisation had, nevertheless, come to stay.

And the Hartley Disaster, as John Wilson points out in his **History,** was a potent factor in "preparing men's minds for such an institution." There were local strikes which played their more immediate part in the drive towards unity, but the leaven was working before those events occurred.

We see early evidence of this reborn faith in the wisdom of workers acting together for the protection of their interests, in the delegate meeting held in Newcastle even before the Hartley dead were buried.

This took place in Newcastle on 25th January, 1862, in the Lecture Room, Nelson Street, a stone's throw from Grey's Monument. Mr. W. Grieves, a miner, presided. Those present were, in the main, miners delegates. The meeting originated out of one of the many pit-head meetings held at Hartley, and although this was the first of its kind to be held in Newcastle following the disaster, several others were to follow in the ensuing weeks.

126

Reference was made to the meeting held in the Guildhall, Newcastle, the previous day when the Lord Mayor of Newcastle was in attendance. Then the business was primarily that of launching the Relief Fund. To-day the emphasis was on the vital question of safety in the pits.

There was a theatrical atmosphere about the occasion. Not theatrical in the sense of the artificial theatre, for here to-day verily, was a drama of real life. Even from the press reports of the meeting one can sense the tension engendered by the importunity of long-suffering men.

The feeling of the meeting was united to a man concerning the ends they all sought. Yet despite this there was, nevertheless, scope for that clash of character, that cut and thrust of debate, that passionate advocacy of a righteous cause, which enlivens any purposive meeting.

The cry for justice was eloquently expressed; it involved the indictment of "a system," and above all it was indicative of the fact that life and death issues were here mightily involved, and that wrongs urgently clamoured for redress by legislative enactment at Westminster. And woe betide the person or the power that dare stand in the way.

The description given here is in the main taken from reports given in the Newcastle **Courant.** I am aware that Fynes gives an account of this meeting, probably also taken from the newspapers of his day. But the highly important discussions of that afternoon are certainly worthy of repetition.

They were a resolute body of men who were assembled there. Many of them had been mandated by the respective collieries from which they came, and they were pledged to end the murderous system of one-shaft pits. They knew from sad experience that, at the worst, tragedies like that at Hartley could happen at many of their pits, and at the best there was the constant dread of disaster. In other words they often went to the coal face in fear of their lives, such were their forebodings. Why else did the Hartley men, greatly daring, call in the Mines Inspector six months before the disaster occurred there !

In a hall thus charged with emotion on these matters Mr. James Mather of South Shields rose to speak.

A word about Mather would be appropriate here. He was a dedicated man, tireless in his service to the miners. Born in Newcastle, he studied medicine and philosophy in the University of Edinburgh. He was frequently to be found bravely descending pits following explosions, effecting rescues and ministering to those in need. When the St. Hilda Pit at South Shields exploded in 1839, causing the loss of 52 lives, Mather applied himself diligently to a study of its causes. The result was the setting up of the South Shields Committee whose authoritative report was widely acclaimed. The Chairman of this Committee, Mr. Ingham, in evidence before a Parliamentary Select Committee in 1852 said : "The entire merit of the enquiry of the South Shields Committee rests with Mr. Mather, he having been down the South Shields pit immediately after the explosion."

And now Mather begged leave to move . . .

That a Petition be presented to the two Houses of Legislature, praying that a special Committee be appointed to enquire into the general question of colliery accidents with a view to preventing a repetition of the frightful calamities which have recently taken place, and that it is the opinion of this meeting that no colliery should be without two independent means of escape from the mine with a view of securing the safety of the miners.

Mr. Mather swayed his audience with a powerful speech. He began with a restrained and quiet sincerity. The miners were not, he said, the intelligent men he conceived them to be, if they had not learned a lesson from this dreadful experience.

It was right and proper to provide for the relief of distress, but it was infinitely more important to learn the lessons taught by these calamities so as to prevent their recurrence. It was a proud thing for him to be present at the Guildhall meeting yesterday and to behold the fine, generous, manly feelings displayed there. It was a particularly happy experience to hear that great coalowner Lord Durham make the remarks which he made, and to see the deep emotion with which he made

THE LIST OF THE DEAD

ERECTED

TO THE MEMORY OF THE 204 MINERS, WHO LOST THEIR LIVES IN HARTLEY PIT, BY THE FATAL CATASTROPHE OF THE ENGINE BEAM BREAKING, 16TH JANUARY 1862.

J. AMOUR.	AGED 43	C. WANLESS.	AGED 20
R. AMOUR.	AGED 14	T. WANLESS.	AGED 19
J. TERNENT.	AGED 44	J. WANLESS.	AGED 14
C. TERNENT.	AGED 15	W. JACK.	AGED 24
W. PAPE.	AGED 14	W. GLEDSON.	AGED 71
T. SHARP.	AGED 48	W. GLEDSON.	AGED 43
H. SHARP.	AGED 44	C. GLEDSON.	AGED 41
A. ELLIOTT.	AGED 29	T. GLEDSON.	AGED 36
C. SHARP.	AGED 49	T. GLEDSON.	AGED 16
G. SHARP.	AGED 15	W. LIDDLE.	AGED 40
J. SHARP.	AGED 13	W. LIDDLE.	AGED 17
J. BEWICK.	AGED 34	J. LIDDLE.	AGED 15
J. BEWICK.	AGED 32	J. LIDDLE.	AGED 16
R. BEWICK.	AGED 30	T. LIDDLE.	AGED 18
T. ROBINSON.	AGED 42	C. LIDDLE.	AGED 16
T. DAWSON.	AGED 49	J. LIDDLE.	AGED 11
J. DAWSON.	AGED 12	T. LIDDLE.	AGED 41
A. RICHARDSON.	AGED 22	T. LIDDLE.	AGED 18
J. JOHNSON.	AGED 41	T. LAWS.	AGED 33
R. JOHNSON.	AGED 42	C. LAWS.	AGED 23
T. COAL.	AGED 37	W. LOUGE.	AGED 30
T. CHAMBERS.	AGED 55	J. LONG.	AGED 15
C. CHAMBERS.	AGED 19	R. LONG.	AGED 17
J. HUMBLE.	AGED 27	M. MURRAY.	AGED 26
W. DIXON.	AGED 34	R. MURLEY.	AGED 23

BLESSED ARE THE DEAD WHICH DIE IN THE LORD. REV. XIV...XIII

"IN THE MIDST OF LIFE WE ARE IN DEATH."

W. BANNAN.	AGED 24	W. ALLAN.	AGED 36
T. BROWN.	AGED 25	A. ATKINSON.	AGED 20
R. BROWN.	AGED 15	W. ALDERTON.	ACED 31
M. BELL.	AGED 23	J. AINSLEY.	AGED 19
T. BELL.	AGED 13	J. ARMSTRONG.	AGED 36
T. BELL.	AGED 23	E. ARMSTRONG.	AGED 12
J. BURN.	AGED 52	J. ARMSTRONG.	AGED 10
T. BURN.	AGED 18	W. ANDERSON.	AGED 17
J. BENNET.	AGED 25	J. BROADFOOT.	AGED 19
J. CAMPBELL.	AGED 28	G. BROWN.	AGED 31
J. COULSON.	AGED 33	W. BROWN.	AGED 25
R. COULSON.	AGED 26	S. BIRTLEY.	AGED 24
A. CHEETHAM.	AGED 33	S. BLACKBURN.	AGED 26
G. CARLING.	AGED 27	H. CLOUGH.	AGED 47
P. CROSS.	AGED 59	J. COUSINS.	AGED 18
P. CROSS.	AGED 20	R. COUSINS.	AGED 12
J. COYLE.	AGED 41	W. DIXON.	AGED 27
J. DAVIDSON.	AGED 38	R. DIXON.	AGED 12
W. DAVIDSON.	AGED 11	J. DOUGLAS.	AGED 25
P. DUFFY.	AGED 34	E. ELLIOTT.	AGED 19
J. DUFFY.	AGED 10	J. FOSTER.	AGED 18
G. FULTON.	AGED 25	J. FOSTER.	AGED 15
J. FORD.	AGED 27	W. FAIRBAIRN.	AGED 70
H. FORD.	AGED 32	G. FAIRBAIRN.	AGED 33
P. FORD.	AGED 12	J. GALLACHER.	AGED 32
G. HAYS.	AGED 41	D. GALLACHER.	AGED 28

THE LIST OF THE DEAD.

THEREFORE BE YE ALSO READY: FOR IN SUCH AN HOUR AS YE THINK NOT THE SON OF MAN COMETH.

MATTHEW XXIV—XLIV

BE NOT DECEIVED: GOD IS NOT MOCKED: FOR WHAT-SOEVER A MAN SOWETH, THAT SHALL HE ALSO REA[P]

GALAS VI—VII[.]

Pᵗ MANDERSON. AGED 50	Wᵐ PALMER. AGED 35	Jᵗ TERNEY. AGED 14	Wᵗ TIBBS. AGED 32
Wᵐ MILLER. AGED 43	Tᵗ RUTHERFORD AGED 22	Cᵗ GRAHAM. AGED 27	Jᵗ TRYER. AGED 33
Wᵐ MILLER. AGED 34	Mᵗ ROBINSON. AGED 30	Cᵗ GLEN. AGED 12	Wᵗ TERNENT. AGED 40
Tᵗ MACAULEY. AGED 38	Wᵐ REDPATH. AGED 24	Wᵗ GLEN. AGED 14	Tᵗ VEITCH. AGED 21
Rᵗ McMULLON. AGED 27	Eᵗ ROWLEY. AGED 33	Jᵗ GLEN. AGED 18	Tᵗ WATSON. AGED 30
Jᵗ MULLON. AGED 36	Wᵐ RUTHERFORD AGED 23	Oᵗ GLECHORN. AGED 24	Cᵗ WILSON. AGED 38
Rᵗ McCLUTCHEY. AGED 24	Jᵗ RUTHERFORD AGED 25	Rᵗ HILL. AGED 21	Bᵗ WALKER. AGED 21
Wᵐ MACFARLANE. AGED 15	Hᵗ RILEY. AGED 30	Pᵗ CORMERLY. AGED 25	Jᵗ WATSON. AGED 16
Jᵗ McKEE. AGED 55	Rᵗ ROBSON. AGED 36	Hᵗ GIBSON. AGED 16	Jᵗ WATSON. AGED 38
Aᵐ McKEE. AGED 24	Jᵗ ROBSON. AGED 12	Fᵗ HAUXWELL. AGED 25	Cᵗ WADE. AGED 31
Wᵐ McCRACHEN. AGED 24	Tᵗ ROSS. AGED 46	Gᵗ HOWARD. AGED 20	Tᵗ WEIRS. AGED 40
Rᵗ NORTH. AGED 26	Rᵗ RANDALL. AGED 33	Jᵗ HARDING. AGED 15	Rᵗ WEIRS. AGED 20
Gᵗ NORTH. AGED 10	Hᵗ MASON. AGED 24	Tᵗ HARRISON. AGED 16	Pᵗ WALPOOL. AGED 30
Aᵗ NORTH. AGED 14	Eᵗ STAINSBY. AGED 23	Gᵗ HALL. AGED 25	Jᵗ WATSON. AGED 39
Aᵗ NORTH. AGED 12	Rᵗ SMALL. AGED 19	Pᵗ HAMMEL. AGED 33	Tᵗ WATSON. AGED 31
Jᵗ NICHOLSON. AGED 52	Tᵗ SEBASTIAN. AGED 19	Tᵗ HEPPLE. AGED 27	Wᵗ WILSON. AGED 16
Jᵗ NICHOLSON. AGED 21	Pᵗ SHERLOCK. AGED 28	Cᵗ HILL. AGED 31	Jᵗ WILKINSON. AGED 23
Jᵗ ORMSTON. AGED 32	Wᵗ STANLEY AGED 34	Cᵗ HINDMARCH. AGED 30	Wᵗ WHITE. AGED 16
Pᵗ NESBIT. AGED 20	Fᵗ SMITH. AGED 33	Aᵗ HOUSTON. AGED 34	Wᵗ WILSON. AGED 12
Jᵗ NICHOLSON. AGED 14	Wᵗ SMITH. AGED 19	Jᵗ HAMELTON. AGED 56	Jᵗ WALKER. AGED 16
Wᵗ OLIVER. AGED 56	Gᵗ SCURFIELD. AGED 52	Jᵗ HAMELTON. AGED 12	Wᵗ WALKER. AGED 12
Jᵗ OLIVER. AGED 27	Eᵗ SOFTLEY. AGED 17	Jᵗ HODGE. AGED 33	Hᵗ YOUNGER. AGED 33
Jᵗ OLIVER. AGED 21	Cᵗ SKINNER. AGED 14	Hᵗ HUNTER. AGED 13	Jᵗ YOUNC. AGED 25
Wᵗ OLIVER. AGED 17	Wᵗ TELFORD. AGED 24	Wᵗ KENNEDY. AGED 30	Jᵗ YOULL. AGED 28
Pᵗ OLIVER. AGED 15	Jᵗ TAYLOR. AGED 36	Aᵗ MORGAN. AGED 14	Dᵗ WYPHER. AGED 24
Tᵗ PEARSON. AGED 28	Gᵗ THIRLWELL. AGED 27		

In this impressive list of the 204 men and boys lost in the Hartley Disaster will be seen the names of boys of ten [...]

them. He wished Lord Durham would oftener show himself to the public with such noble sentiments.

But it was not only the present misfortune, unparalleled as it was in the history of mining which focussed attention on the necessity of the resolution which he submitted to the meeting. There were too many of these tragedies constantly happening.

"Take Burradon", he said. And when James Mather mentioned Burradon the meeting to a man sighed sadly and made gutteral sounds of indignation. Burradon was local, fresh in their minds, and heated controversies had raged about the bad state of the pit's ventilation prior to the explosion there.

"Take Burradon", repeated Mather, and as he did so he warmed to his subject the more. What caused the men to be destroyed at Burradon ? It was not the time to mince matters. He blamed no individual man. **It was the system that was to blame !** This system was the most destructive of human life ever devised by man. It was wealth against human life, and now is the time to put an end to it (loud applause).

Speaking with knowledge from his great experience of mine disasters, Mr. Mather went on to say that about half the men lost in mine disasters were lost from the effects of after-damp. One inspector of mines giving evidence before a House of Commons Committee put the proportion as high as 70%. Now choke-damp took some time to spread over the floors and passages of the mine, and the men were obliged to breathe it until they succumbed. He would say that 40 to 50 of the 75 men lost at Burradon were lost in that way. And the men at Hartley were obliged to breathe poisoned air until they likewise succumbed. Had there been a second shaft at Hartley, the life of every man and boy would have been spared—they would have been restored to the bosoms of their families within a matter of hours after the breaking of that beam. Was it not of the utmost importance that the means should be available at every mine for the rescue of the men in a situation such as that at Hartley ? (Applause).

He spoke appreciatively of the generous subscriptions to the Relief Fund which were coming from all quarters. But had fifty of those men been spared for twenty more years they would have raised more money than all the public subscriptions put together.

Mr. Mather said he wanted to rouse the miners to the sense of duty which they owed to themselves and to their families, "God helps those who help themselves, you know"—and if determined action that day was the beginning of a great movement, success would be assured in this great cause.

Let them go to Parliament, let them appeal to the great British public, let them show what was being done in the best laid-out mines, for he was only a bungling viewer who sank a one-shaft pit, and concentrated on a single shaft all the efforts of his intelligence.

He stood here to-day in the presence of a man well able to judge these matters. He referred to Mr. Matthias Dunn. Perhaps he would not want to give his opinion about the cost of the sinking of a second shaft at Hartley—for they were very delicate these official men, these inspectors (laughter). But he himself ventured to say that a mere £2,000 would have put in a second shaft at Hartley. Difficult sinkings cost £20 per fathom to sink, and Hartley being a hundred fathoms deep, that meant £2,000. And for the want of that outlay they must have this hecatomb of men and a great subscription from the British public.

Mr. Mather repeated that he did not blame the owners individually, it was the system that was to blame. This system too was spreading. Even now when they should be perpetually learning from experience, they were actually sinking, within gun-shot, or at least within an Armstrong gun-shot (a topical allusion to the progress of British armament) solitary brattice pits, where the first explosion which took place, or the first accident that happened to the brattice, would hasten miners to their doom forty and fifty at a time. Was that to go on for ever ? (loud cries of "No"). How long are you going to tolerate that state of affairs ? He protested most emphatically, as a British subject, against such a barbaric system (loud and prolonged applause).

130

Mr. Mather then mentioned other local mining calamities in which lives had been lost due to the want of a second shaft. These included Wallsend and the St. Hilda Pit at South Shields. A strong body of opinion was building up in support of this campaign for a second shaft. He could mention three of the most intelligent inspectors in the country who supported the resolution now before them. Nay, Her Majesty's Government had already been moved to act. He had seen a note to Mr. Dunn from the Home Secretary, which showed that concern was reaching high places. And the **Times** newspaper with its magnificent power had come down on their side. A very able article there advocated the necessity of two shafts. A house on fire should have two doors, one at the front and one at the back—an emergency exit. Some owners said it would cost £10,000 or £12,000 to sink another shaft, but that estimate included surface equipment for drawing coal as well. It was not for coal drawing that a second shaft was needed. Not for money-making and profit. It was for the ventilation of the pit. It was to provide a way of escape. Its purpose was for the saving of life (applause).

As evidence that the Government was being compelled to act Mr. Mather quoted a *Circular from the Home Office received by Mr. Dunn which required him to state the number of single bratticed shafts in his district and the practicability of requiring that all large collieries should have two shafts. The mines inspectors have a difficult job to do but he would dearly like to see their replies to this Circular.

Mr. Mather said that before he sat down he felt he must defend Mr. Dunn against the unfair criticism to which he had been subjected of late. He had used to the full such powers as he had, of which the ladder from the Low Main to the Yard Seam at Hartley was an example. He moved the Resolution. This was seconded by Mr. Joseph Cowan, junior, and was carried "amid great applause."

* This circular dated 24th January, 1862, was superseded by another one on the same subject on 28th January—see Appendix No. 4.

At a later stage of this great meeting lively dialogues took place between miners in the body of the hall and Mr. Dunn on the platform. These reflected the strength of feeling then prevailing about Hartley. No playwright could better express the crisply dramatic exchanges which took place.

The drama began as follows. A miner from the floor made a speech attacking Mr. Dunn. Mr. Dunn, he said, knew the state of affairs at Hartley. If he hadn't the legal power to remedy the matter, he ought to have laid the position before the public. (Applause and remarks such as, "That's the point", "That's the rub", etc.).

Mr. Dunn answered his critic. He had not, at present, the power to compel the owners to provide two shafts. In 1858 at a meeting of inspectors in Manchester, he had suggested that reports on these matters should be made by inspectors. There was a lot of talk but no resolution. The pitmen themselves could help by calling in the inspector more than they did.

It was at this point that the lively exchanges began :

A Miner : I believe you have something like 150 collieries to inspect ?

Mr. Dunn : Yes.

Miner : Twenty-eight in Cumberland ?

Mr. Dunn : Yes.

Miner : Do you think you are able to inspect all those ?

Mr. Dunn : Well, the Government think I am able, you know. (Laughter).

Miner : Well then, Sir, I have heard a complaint that you are too old to fill the office you hold (uproar and cries of "Shame", "Perfectly right", "Sit down", "No, I will not").

When things quietened down a bit the Inspector gave his answer—a soft answer calculated to turn away wrath . . .

Mr. Dunn : You know, Sir, if I am very old I should be very experienced. I may say that I am the most experienced of any of the inspectors; they all admit that.

Another miner now rose to his feet to press home the questioning . . .

Another Miner : Were you satisfied with the one shaft at this colliery ? If so, that is the end of the matter. If not what steps did you take to remedy the defect ? Did you apply to the Secretary of State showing him that it was defective ?

Mr. Dunn : At this very moment there are three of the largest collieries in Northumberland, namely Seaton Delaval, North Seaton and Newsham, all managed by the most talented men in Northumberland, and all with single shafts. Now what would you have me to do ? Do you think it my duty to call in question the management of all these men ?

Miner : Is that an answer to my question whether you are satisfied with the single shaft ?

Mr. Dunn : Well, I am not so well satisfied as if they had two, but I have not the power to alter it.

Miner : Have you no power to apply to the Secretary of State ?

Mr. Dunn : What would I say to the Secretary of State ?

Miner : Tell him that it is dangerous to the lives of the miners in the pits not having two shafts.

Here the chairman came to the rescue. He intervened to stop the discussion. But he also took the opportunity of referring to Mr. Dunn's advice to the men to call in the inspector more often than they did. The trouble was that when they did, they had no protection. **When they dared to speak up they were sacked** (applause). He had no doubt that if the public understood their position they would support the men in advocating reform in the mines.

This remarkable meeting was now addressed by a visitor from London. It was indicative of those elements in our British democracy which have so often stood for decency and fairplay in the face of injustice.

This gentleman had travelled hot-foot, as it were, overnight. He represented well-disposed gentlemen in the Metropolis. And he came with fifty guineas in his pocket (for the Hartley Relief Fund) and, more important, a mandate to speak up on behalf of the oppressed and suffering victims of the present coal-mining system.

As we have already indicated the miners were in dire need of influential allies. Soon a lasting trade union was to be

133

hammered out on the anvil of experience, but as yet there was scope for the help of the benevolent philanthropist. That altruistic interest which prompted some well-meaning upper class people to lend a hand to those less fortunate was timely and welcome.

So it was that Mr. G. A. Towers of London mounted the platform. He said he attended the meeting on behalf of the National Association for the Relief of British Miners. He had travelled all night from London at the request of that powerful social reformer Lord Shaftesbury, who, along with Sir Fitzroy Kelly and others, was taking a deep interest in the welfare of the British miner. As a first instalment towards the requirements of these poor people he was requested by the gentlemen concerned to place in the hands of the Committee the sum of fifty guineas (applause).

As he went on to speak it became evident that Mr. Towers had come all the way to Newcastle not out of a morbid interest in the Hartley affair, nor indeed as a kind of relieving officer, but that he had a more radical and constructive purpose to fulfil. Greatly daring, but with painstaking politeness, he too attacked Mr. Dunn, the mines inspector.

He was not quite satisfied, he said, that Her Majesty's inspectors of mines had not a great deal more power than Mr. Dunn had made out. He held in his hand a Digest of the Acts of Parliament for the Regulation of Coal Mines and with great diffidence he read the following clause :

> Each inspector acts within his own district; he may enquire into the state and condition of the mine, the ventilation, mode of lighting, etc., in any such mine, and **into all matters connected with the Safety of all persons there employed** (applause).

Mr. Towers thought that last clause was a very sweeping clause and he repeated that he ventured to submit it with great diffidence in the presence of Mr. Dunn. After remarking that England's Mines made England's wealth, and that her miners had done more than any other class to promote her greatness as a nation, he proceeded to point out how little had been done to ensure the safety of the men who produced the coal. It was not merely reform that was wanted, it was a total reconstruction (applause).

If Her Majesty's inspectors were not numerous enough to pay that proper attention which was necessary to provide for the safety of the miner then it became the duty of the British public to urge on the Legislature that more should be appointed to provide as far as human agency could, for the prevention of these fearful calamities (loud applause).

There were votes of thanks and a memorable meeting was terminated. It had been abundantly worthwhile this demonstration. So dynamic, so full of high purpose, it epitomized in its tense dramatic sequences, and its assertion of basic human rights, so much that is to be treasured in our British way of life.

Chapter 5

THE COMPULSION ON THE LEGISLATURE

If, as the **Times** said, the Hartley Disaster was "A spectacle and a thought to possess the mind of a nation"—and such it proved to be—it was inevitable that the resulting universal concern should culminate in a measure of remedial legislation.

And so it came about that on the 7th August, 1862, just seven months after the disaster occurred, a special Act of Parliament was passed which made it compulsory for every mine to have two shafts.

In January of that year the **Times** had remarked: "How so obvious a precaution (as a second shaft) came to be overlooked we know not."

But it was not really overlooked. The attention of the coal-owners generally had long ago, and repeatedly, been drawn to the elementary necessity of providing a second shaft.

True, the emphasis in the early days had been on the second shaft as a means of better ventilation rather than as an emergency exit. Sidney Webb tells us that exactly 200 years before Hartley, in 1662, two thousand miners of the Tyne and Wear put their marks to a petition to the King, praying for the redress of their grievances foremost among which was the danger to which they were exposed by insufficient ventilation of the pits. This was followed fourteen years later (1676) by a second petition. It was at this time that the King's Minister, Lord Keeper North, made his well-known and quaintly-worded but significant pronouncement about fire damp. "Damps or foul airs kill insensibly. **Sinking another pit that the airs may not stagnate is an infallible remedy.**"

Thereafter the question of the necessity of the second shaft kept cropping up in the wake of disasters. For instance we meet with it in the Minutes of Evidence of the Select Committee on Accidents in Coal Mines which reported to Parliament in

1835. But the old argument that the expense of providing a second shaft would cause the closing down of the pits, was put to the Committee by Mr. John Buddle the well-known North-country mining engineer . . .

> When gentlemen have expended £50,000 to £60,000 in sinking one pit, it might not be convenient to expend £20,000 more in sinking another, merely to avoid the chance of any accident that might eventually happen. In fact I conceive if there were any legislative interference on that point it would tend to extinguish a very large proportion of our coal mines.

On the other hand it was to the credit of the great George Stephenson (of railway fame) in his submission to the same Committee that he favoured the compulsion of law to enforce the provision of two shafts. Two shafts, he said, would ensure more perfect ventilation than one bratticed shaft, and he felt it a matter of sufficient importance to justify legislative inter-ference. "Interference!" That word was abhorrent to the coal-owners. "Hands off the pits,,' they said, and they meant it. The first Safety Law, the Mines Regulation Act of 1850, was passed, as Webb points out, in the teeth of the embittered opposition of the coalowners. Such was the hostility shown, that a special clause was inserted in the Act, expressly requiring the coal-owners to allow the inspectors entrance to, and egress from, the mines, because Lord Londonderry had publicly declared that he would not allow any inspector to go down his pits, and that if an inspector did go down he might stay there !

The historian Welbourne, in his work, **The Miners' Unions of Northumberland and Durham** describes the hostility of the coalowners to Government interference as "fanatical" :—

> How fanatical was the opposition to interference is shewn by the refusal to adopt a system of registration of mine surveys, though Buddle, the foremost viewer in the north, gave it his support and pointed out how rapidly the danger of inundation from old workings was growing.

The body of feeling which for years had been building up in the country concerning the need to curb the powers of certain coalowners, had behind it the well-informed conclusions of people like Matthias Dunn himself. Dunn had had a vast experience as a mining engineer in most of the coalfields of Britain as well as of Belgium, and in his book **Winning and Working of Collieries,** published in 1848, he said how concerned he was that vast quantities of the nation's wealth in coal were being "irrevocably lost" by the improper working of the pits. But a still more important consideration was the colossal sacrifice of human life by "repeated explosions" . . .

> As a practical person therefore, I do not hesitate to affirm that instead of interference of Government being deprecated (as it has been by certain persons) it will on the contrary be productive of incalculable benefits.

Experience proved that more and more "interference" was necessary as time went on. The 1850 Act was followed by others in 1855 and in 1860. And just as the miners of 1662 had petitioned the King, so now in 1862, with the horror of Hartley fresh upon them, the miners petitioned Parliament from their meeting in Newcastle for more protective legislation.

Galloway's informative work, **A History of Coal Mining in Great Britain** (pub. 1882), refers to the "Oft repeated condemnation of the system of working collieries by means of a single bratticed shaft".

Several examples are cited including that of the explosion at the St. Hilda Pit, South Shields in June 1839, which led to the setting up of the South Shields Committee, already mentioned, in which James Mather played so great a part.

The South Shields Committee reported in 1843, and Galloway describes the Report as "a most able and valuable document, remarkably correct, sound, sagacious and practical". That Committee, says Galloway, recommended that "No new mine should be allowed to be worked unless two distinct and separate shafts had previously been put down, which should be secured by Act of Parliament".

Meanwhile, Galloway continues, colliery explosions continued to alarm the mining community, and the miners once more petitioned the House of Commons in March 1845. In August of that year another Commission was appointed by Parliament consisting of Sir H. T. de la Beche and Dr. Lyon Playfair. Even while the Commissioners were busy conducting their enquiry another two serious explosions occurred, one at Jarrow Colliery in Durham and the other at Risca in South Wales, and special instructions were issued to the Commissioners to take on the additional work of investigating the causes of these explosions.

In the course of their Report submitted in June 1846, the Commissioners, Galloway informs us, "endorsed the condemnation of the system of working a colliery by means of a single shaft, the evils of which had recently been witnessed in the case of the explosion at Jarrow, adding that similar dangers existed where two shafts were insufficiently separated, as was the case at Risca in South Wales".

Another serious explosion quickly followed at the Ardsley Main or Oaks Colliery, near Barnsley in March 1847, by which 73 lives were lost. Sir H. T. de la Beche and Mr. Warington Smyth investigated the circumstances of this event, and drew up a joint Report dated 22nd March 1847. One point of criticism in the report was that the shafts were too near to each other (being only nine feet apart) in consequence of which the force of the blast from the explosion breached them at a weak point.

The above is but a selection from a long list of such disasters catalogued by Galloway. Hence it is not to be wondered at that he sums up the situation as follows :—

> Notwithstanding the oft repeated condemnation of the system of working collieries by means of a single bratticed shaft, no steps had as yet been taken to put an end to the practice. In January 1862, however, the long list of calamities arising from this defective arrangement culminated in the great catastrophe at Hartley Colliery in Northumberland, when two hundred and four persons lost their lives by the half of the beam of the pumping engine breaking off and falling down the pit wrecking the brattice and destroying the ventilation, and cutting off all communication with the surface. This at length led to the passing of a short Act of Parliament prohibiting collieries from being worked unless provided with at least two means of exit, separated by not less than ten feet of natural strata.

The demand for the elementary precaution of the second shaft could no longer be resisted. Mr. Kenyon Blackwell, the Mines Inspector, aware of the historic stubbornness of the coalowners, might equivocate somewhat in his report to the Home

Secretary, but as Simonin, referring to this attitude of Blackwell in his book **Mines and Miners,** says: "The English legislature paid no attention to these observations", and added that the English had a tendency to borrow from the French some of their restrictive measures. In other words to "interfere" where the necessity was proven. The truth of the matter was that the Government simply dare not refuse to interfere, for they knew that the miners had the sympathy of the whole nation.

It is instructive to probe into Parliament's attitude to this matter. When I reached this stage in my researches, I felt I must observe carefully the reaction of Parliament to the whole problem thus posed by Hartley. True, the Home Secretary, Sir George Grey, had sent out fact-finding circulars to mines inspectors up and down the land, and he had also given carefully worded directions to Inspector Blackwell who represented him at the Inquest.

But a perusal of **Hansard's Parliamentary Debates** for 1862 reveals pathetically little to show that Parliament shared the profound indignation evident in the country concerning Hartley.

Feeling that there might be somewhere in official files Parliamentary documents which could possibly reveal more fully Westminster's concern about Hartley, I enlisted the aid of our local M.P., Mr. W. R. Blyton, one ever willing to render all possible assistance.

In my letter to him I set out such knowledge as I had gleaned from Hansard and asked if there was more to it than that. The following is an extract from his letter in reply : "I have had the Librarians of the House of Commons and the House of Lords working on the letter you sent me re the Hartley Disaster . . . They assure me after a day's research that you have all the information relative to the matter."

To return to my perusal of Hansard, I found that on June 12th, 1862, a question was put to the Home Secretary by a Mr. Dillwyn who asked : "Whether it is the intention of Government to introduce any measure to amend the Law relative to the working of Coal Mines?"

"Sir George Grey said a Bill was in preparation which would be ready in a few days, the object of which would be not so much to interfere with the general working of mines, as to provide for the construction of a second shaft in cases where that was practicable."

This promised Bill was accordingly introduced. No debate took place on the First, Second or Third Readings in the Commons. Nor did any debate take place in the First and Second Readings in the Lords. Only on the Third Reading in the Lords was there an awakening of interest in the passage of the Bill. That was on the 24th July, 1862 when Earl de Grey and Ripon moved to insert an Amendment—fortunately a harmless one. In so doing he hoped the Home Secretary would show every indulgence to the coalowners for their willingness to co-operate in this measure.

The hearts of some of the noble Lords appeared to be more concerned for the unfettered preservation of their economic privileges than for any implications which Hartley might have for them.

Lord Ravensworth, for instance, a powerful northern coal-owner was constrained to speak on the Third Reading. His Lordship had great possessions in the heart of the northern coalfield. His ancestral home, Ravensworth Castle near Gateshead, had been rebuilt from designs by Nash in 1808 and his father had been a patron of George Stephenson. Before succeeding to the title in 1855 Lord Ravensworth (formerly known as Henry Thomas Liddell) had spent huge sums of money on elections, and represented North Durham in Parliament from 1837 to 1847. The restrained language of the **Dictionary of National Biography** says of him: "He steadily from 1829 opposed the Reform Movement." An example of this opposition to reform was given on 30th June, 1847 when Mr. T. S. Duncombe moved his "Mines and Collieries Bill" in the House of Commons. Its chief purpose was to ensure better ventilation of coal mines. Mr. Liddell (North Durham) was one of those dead against it, and the measure was withdrawn. Mr.

Liddell wanted the Bill put off until a later date which provoked the following retort from a member supporting the Bill :

> Mr. Wakley (Finsbury) said the interests of the poor were always staved off, but if one noble lord had been blown out of a coal pit, instead of hundreds of miners, not only would a measure have been at once introduced, but he doubted if the matter would not have been mentioned in the speech from the Throne (much laughter).

Even Hartley could not silence this voice of Reaction. Here is the report from Hansard :

> Lord Ravensworth called attention to the circumstances that although this measure would impose some restraints upon the working of coal mines, it had received no opposition from the coalowners, and expressed a hope that in the working of the Bill every indulgence would be shown to those whose peculiar position might render it necessary.

In reply, Earl de Grey and Ripon admitted that **nothing but a strong case of necessity** could justify the passing of such a Bill as this, and said he had no doubt that his Right Honourable Friend, the Secretary of State, would, in the administration of the Law, show the indulgence which was due to the coalowners for the manner in which they had received the Bill.

The Amendment was agreed to and the Bill passed.

What did the Act provide ? It was but a short Act with the title :

An Act to Amend the Law Relating to Coal Mines—
7th August, 1862
(25 and 26 Vict. Cap. 79)

The Act related to coal and ironstone mines and provided that after the passing of the Act it was unlawful for the owner of a new mine, and, after 1st January, 1865, unlawful for the owner of an existing mine (i.e. existing at the time the Act came into force) to employ persons in such a mine unless there were at least two shafts or outlets separated by natural strata not less than ten feet in breadth. The shafts had to provide distinct means of ingress and egress to persons employed in the mine.

This special Act was consolidated in the Coal Mines Regulation Act of 1872.

"Nothing", said the Noble Lord, "Nothing but a strong case of necessity" could justify the passing of such an Act.

Thus had Parliament been coerced into the acceptance of this Amendment of the Law. How different its mood and temper from the pit-head meetings at Hartley as the bodies, one by one, were hauled from the pit! And how far removed from the righteous indignation of the Newcastle meeting described in an earlier chapter of this book.

But at least it can be said that the 204 men of Hartley did not die in vain. A Statute of the Realm bears testimony to the truth of that.

Mr. DAVID WILKINSON

Mr. WILLIAM SHIELDS

Mr. GEORGE EMMERSON

THREE OF THE HARTLEY HEROES

ook at their manly, courageous, resolute faces", said a speaker about the sinkers
the presentation of their medals. There is abundant confirmation of that opinion
the above pictures of three of the leading sinkers.

PHOTO-COPY BY J. C. CURRY

FORGOTTEN SPOT

Writing in 1912, T. E. Forster said :

"The shaft, in which the cause of the calamity, the half of the broken beam, still lies buried, is marke by a stone wall surrounding it, in which the date stone of the old pumping engine house has bee inserted".

Above is a photograph of the spot taken by the author in the summer of 1962. M George Carse, a deputy-overman, paid off with the final closing of Hartley Collier in 1959, kindly posed for me.

There is about this place all the sadness of a deserted shrine. Obscured by th surrounding kitchen plots of the adjacent houses (Hester Gardens) cold frames, etc clutter up its approaches. It is indeed depressing to think that this once hallowe spot where, watched by a waiting world, one of the bravest epics of our industri history was enacted, is now so lost and forlorn. The glory has departed—can not be restored ?

PHOTO (1962) BY J. E. McCUTCHEO

GOOD TIMES, BAD TIMES, ALL TIMES GET OVER

From an engraving by Bewick.   PHOTO-COPY BY J. C. CURR

PART FIVE

The Day of Reward

Chapter 1

COULSON'S MEN OF COURAGE

It is time for us to return from that "other-world" atmosphere of Westminster, back to the familiar ground of the coalfield.

What the press described as the final act in the many demonstrations of public feeling in connection with the Hartley catastrophe, took place on Tuesday, 20th May, 1862.

This was a social occasion convened in Newcastle, the purpose of which was to do honour to the sinkers whose heroism and fortitude was by now a household word throughout the land.

There was no doubt about the universal esteem in which the sinkers were held. It is opportune here to list a few of the tributes which were forthcoming from all sides.

There was the tribute of the jury at the Inquest. The jury felt obliged to "Notice with admiration the heroic courage of the viewers and others, who, at the risk of their own lives, for so many nights and days, devoted their best skill and energy to rescue the unfortunate men who were lost".

Then there was the letter written on behalf of the Home Secretary to Mr. Kenyon Blackwell, which said, "The most melancholy feature in the present case is the failure of the unremitting efforts made with the greatest courage and perseverance under circumstances of much difficulty and danger, to save the lives of any of the large number of persons shut into the pit by the closing of the shaft."

And when James Mather paid the following tribute to the courage of miners in general, he doubtless had in mind the type of behaviour exemplified by the Hartley men :

Deeds have been done in the darkness of the mine, and amidst the most appalling dangers, which ennoble our common nature, and which, if done in the light of day and before the world, would have covered those humble miners with glory

147

Mr. Wemyss Reid, as indicated earlier in this book, gave the sinkers unstinted praise. He spoke of the "calm grandeur of heroism" with which the sinkers went about their work. He cited individual cases like that of the sinker Emmerson who "laboured in the shaft and out of it, continuously from Friday morning until late on Monday night without getting one hour's sleep"; he spoke of these sinkers labouring frantically, as few men have laboured before, "their lives the while hanging by a slender thread," and he asserted that "accidents like this call forth the noblest qualities of the Northumbrian miner, some incidents having transpired which belong to the heroic and are deserving of being written in letters of gold."

Yet another glowing tribute was paid by no less a person than the Bishop of Durham, the Right Rev. Dr. Baring. Dr. Baring went to Hartley, visited the bereaved, and talked to the sinkers. And at the great meeting at the Newcastle Guildhall on 24th January, 1862, held for the purpose of launching the Relief Fund, the Bishop spoke in terms of high praise of the Hartley sinkers. The Lord Mayor of Newcastle presided, and the distinguished gathering included the Earl of Durham and other lords and gentry.

One significant feature of this tribute of the Bishop's was that the industrial hero had suddenly become valued at his true worth. At a time when the "Soldiers of the Queen" were without rival in popular esteem, we now have a recognition of the fact, that these ordinary workers were somehow endowed with comparable qualities. As will be seen, this thought runs through all the speech-making and the press comments of that time.

Appealing for the best possible support to be given to the Relief Fund the Bishop spoke as follows:

> Let me say that we owe this effort not only to the sufferers but to those noble and heroic men who during the past nine days have been working at the risk of their own lives to save the poor prisoners.
>
> We can hardly realise what a noble task these men have undertaken. Only two men can work in the shaft, suspended by a rope, and one of them with whom I was speaking yesterday, told me that all the support they had was to sit on a piece of wood not the length of his arm. All the while a torrent of cold water poured

down the shaft to produce a due supply of oxygen. This is the condition in which these men are working for two hours, exposed to the further risk of stone falling from the side of the shaft, or suffocation by the ascending stythe. Yet these noble men have risked their lives day by day patiently. And what a fearful thing it is to think that some persons around the pit were saying the men were not doing their duty as they ought, and were murmuring rather than blessing them for their work. I saw three of these men in the houses I visited yesterday; they were simple, humble men, having no pride in their work, and speaking just as if there was not a man in the world but would have done as they were doing. In the last cottage I visited there was one fine fellow who had been down the pit on Thursday night rather more than two hours, there having been some slight delay in his being relieved. His face I saw was swollen with the gas, yet there he was clad again in his pit clothes to go down at six o'clock last night! I say such men are our real heroes (applause) Northumberland may well be proud of them. The whole country may well be proud of them. I would sooner shake hands with such men than with those who show bravery of another kind—not in saving but in slaying human beings (loud applause).

The Bishop then went on to speak of the "true heroes too amongst those who had perished."

This thought of the Bishop's about the miners being as valiant as any soldier, also ran through the columns of the press. The **Times** asked, "Shall we celebrate victories in the field and not do honour to heroism in the dark and deadly pit?" And again, "There is no feat of war that can surpass such deeds." The theme is further developed in the **Times** with the following really splendid tribute :

As peace has its battles it has too its utter and lamentable defeats. All is lost at Hartley. The whole science and heroism of a province have been brought to bear on the few cubic yards of rubbish that shut in 200 grand and honest lives from their fellow men, and they have failed. All Northumberland would have gone to the breach had the space permitted though it were to work deep in that treacherous pit under falling water, with stones and crazy woodwork thundering overhead, and the still more murderous 'stythe' rising from below.

All these quotations are indicative of the universal esteem in which the sinkers were held. There arose in consequence a spontaneous demand that recognition of their bravery should take some tangible form. Perhaps it was best summed up by no less a person than the Lord Mayor of London, who speaking to the Lord Mayor of Newcastle (who happened to be in London in connection with the Hartley Relief Fund Appeal) said, "What are you doing about those noble men who risked their lives?"

So it came about that the special occasion referred to at the beginning of this chapter was held in Newcastle on 20th May, 1862.

There were two sessions. In the afternoon the sinkers, their wives and their friends were entertained to dinner at Messrs. Brinton & Sons, and this was followed in the evening by a Civic Reception at the Newcastle Town Hall where there were laudatory speeches and presentations.

Doubtless many of those hardy sons of toil would be out of their element listening here in this formal setting to the generous praise which was lavished upon them, for this would be an even greater ordeal to their unassuming natures than that of battling against the dangers of the Hartley pit shaft. But it was a widespread and sincere demand that this honour should be done. So here they were. They sat stiffly in their best clothes, listening to the many voices reciting their eulogies, evoking memories of those nightmare January days in the shaft with all those perils which tested their skill and endurance until the end when the dead were raised up the shaft—a nauseating culmination to a necessary job of work.

The presentations took the form of medals and money. For Mr. Coulson, Senior, a gold medal, for the others, silver medals. A special fund was set up for the purpose, with Mr. T. G. Hurst as its Secretary, and contributions came from all parts of the country. The sum of £1,587 was collected, including £300 which was subscribed by the Committee of the Relief Fund.

The Presentation Committee had from the first decided that the testimonial should take the form of a commemorative medal of some sort, so the services of Mr. Wyon of the Mint were engaged, and his designs subsequently approved. He was then empowered to "execute the dies and strike the medals." After meeting the expenses involved in this work, the balance of the money in the Presentation Fund was divided amongst the sinkers in accordance with the proportion of time each had worked on the rescue operation. The biggest sum paid to any one sinker was £30. Details of the recipients and the amount each received are given in an appendix to this book.

There were two somewhat disappointing features about this great day. One was that the actual medals were not ready in time for handing over and card replicas had to be used instead. The other disappointment was that Mr. Coulson, senior, could not be present, the press report stating: "He is, we believe, engaged on the Continent."

Mr. Hugh Taylor, Chairman of the Coal Trade of Northumberland and Durham, presided, and the speeches made that evening were of a high standard. The chief speech was that given by Mr. Taylor himself.

He retold the essentials of the Hartley story with which readers are already familiar. A few new facts emerged concerning the extent of the coal royalty in which Hartley Colliery was situated.

Mr. Taylor said, for example, that the Hartley coal royalty lay about twelve miles north-east of Newcastle, was very large in extent being of 8,000 or 9,000 acres and belonged to Lord Hastings. The northern part of this was worked by the Seaton Delaval Coal Company, the southern part was unoccupied, and it was the middle portion of about 2,000 acres which was let to Messrs. Carr.

It was in that latter portion that the Hartley Hester Pit was sunk in 1845. Both the Main Coal and the Yard Seam had been extensively worked previously and the whole of these old workings were full of water. This fact was known to the proprietors of the colliery when they began to sink their pit. Hence the need, demonstrated later, of the large pumping engine with its great beam.

The men at Hartley were working in the Low Main, the lowest seam. They had "holed" into the "waste"—that vast area from which the coal had been extracted, and which was now a dangerous underground reservoir. There was always some apprehension, said Mr. Taylor, in approaching a waste of that kind, that the influx of water might overpower them. Hence their reliance on the staple to the Yard Seam, should such an emergency arise.

Then Mr. Taylor made some comments about the coal trade in general—the immense output from our mines, the great loss of miners' lives in the course of this, and England's position in the world which somehow made it worthwhile :

> The Coal Trade of England is a very great and important trade. At the present time I believe we are producing about 80,000,000 tons per year. In the working of that the sacrifice of human life is considerable—800 to 1,000 men per annum. But it is worth some sacrifice to keep England in her position in the world.

It may be that Mr. Taylor in stressing this patriotic sentiment could, inadvertently have laid himself open to the charge of being callous concerning the loss of life in the pits so long as it ministered to England's greatness. But that was surely not what he intended. Yet there were people in high places who thought there was a certain inevitability about the great loss of life in the pits.

The Lord Mayor of Newcastle (Joseph Armstrong, Esq.) moved the adoption of the Report of the Presentation Committee in a speech appropriate to the occasion. It was then that he quoted the Lord Mayor of London as asking "What are you doing about those noble men who risked their lives?"—a question which was followed by the donation of £194 which the Lord Mayor of London collected for the sinkers' Presentation Fund.

The next speaker was the Rev. C. T. Whitley, Vicar of Bedlington, whose speech was full of praise for the sinkers. He thought the lines of Wordsworth's "Happy Warrior" fitted the occasion :

> Who, whether praise of him must walk the earth
> For ever, and to noble deeds give birth,
> Or he must fall to sleep without his fame
> And leave a dead unprofitable name,
> Finds comfort in himself and in his cause,
> And when the mortal mist is gathering, draws
> His breath in confidence of Heaven's applause,
> This is the Happy Warrior, this is he
> Whom every man in arms should wish to be.

"That is the manner of man we honour tonight," said Mr. Whitley, "and one day some likely lads or comely lasses will say, 'That medal was won by my grandfather in the pit at Hartley.'" (applause).

Rev. Dr. Bruce spoke of the sinkers' race with time, for when the waters in the disaster pit were rapidly rising, it was thanks to the sinkers that the loved ones were restored to their families for decent burial.

The sinkers were then called up in succession, and, amid the cheers of the audience received from the hands of the Chairman, the cards entitling them to the medals, together with the sums of money to which they were respectively entitled. Mr. Coulson, Junior, represented his father and received his father's decoration as well as his own.

But the speeches were not yet finished. The liveliest speech of the evening appears to have been that made by Mr. Edward Glyn.

Milton, he said, gave utterance to a line which had passed into common usage in our language—"Peace hath her victories no less renowned than war." And we are here tonight to celebrate one of those victories (loud applause).

Mr. Glyn appealed to his audience to gaze upon the countenances of the sinkers arrayed before them. With his arm extended towards them he said, "Look at their manly, their courageous, their resolute faces!" He then picked up a card and said he bore in his hand the engraving of one of the medals presented that night. It is inscribed, he said, with a name no nobler than that of "John Smith." Yet John Smith might wear that medal and be proud indeed to do so (applause).

For the benefit of his audience, Mr. Glyn described the allegorical design on one side of the medal. It represented a group of miners buried in the earth, above them was the Angel of Death claiming them as victims, and at the same time menacing a second group of miners, who, regardless of their danger, were endeavouring to rescue their fellow workmen. On the reverse side of the medal were the words :

Presented to those who risked their own lives in attempting to save the lives of their fellow workmen buried in Hartley Colliery, January, 1862.

As Mr. Glyn concluded his forceful speech he gave one more example of the industrial hero being compared to his advantage with that of the war-time hero :

We have heard of medals being presented for feats of war; we have heard of medals being presented by the excellent Humane Society for the rescue of lives from shipwreck; we have heard, in London at least of the presentation of medals for the saving of lives from fire, but this is the first time we have heard of medals being presented for the rescue of lives in mining operations. The soldier who wore upon his breast the Victoria Cross or the Waterloo Medal might well be proud of it. But I say that these men here today who wear this Hartley Medal might be as proud of it as if they had gained it at Trafalgar, or Waterloo, or Delhi, or Sebastopol (loud applause).

It was of course to be expected that one of the sinkers would rise to respond to the toasts concerning them. Jack Manderson did so. He spoke simply and sincerely, being better versed in arts other than those concerned with oratory.

He said his own feelings on this occasion were indeed very painful. He stood there as one who, in that awful calamity had lost a dear brother, so that the celebration was overshadowed by a certain solemnity.

Jack Manderson's next thought, though humbly expressed, was akin to those uttered by the great Victor Hugo in his "Toilers of the Sea", and Simonin in his "Mines and Miners", where each views alike the nobility of the toil of the mariner and the miner. "For each" says Simonin, "is a soldier of the deep against whom the powers of nature wage at times their utmost fury."

So, Manderson spoke. In different words but in similar vein. There are two classes of men, he said, who more particularly make up the great bulk of the British people—the sailors and the miners. Both courageously face great perils. The calamity which had brought them together that night, had, he thought, caused the British public to appreciate the more the dangers which the pitmen had to face. "It gives me pleasure" he concluded, "as one who gave his help at the Hartley Pit to try to save his own brother and his fellow-sufferers, to move a vote of thanks to the Committee of Management for their interest in the work of the sinkers expressed in the organisation of this Presentation Ceremony."

And so the great evening of celebration came to an end. It broke up with much hand-shaking and back-slapping, and a good deal of laughter, for they were Happy Warriors these men who could relax despite their manly and resolute faces. But also, one imagines, there would be sighs and tears for the tragedy which had begotten this function.

Nevertheless, it was, after all, a Victory Celebration, for Peace hath her victories no less renowned than war.

Chapter 2

YESTERDAY'S DUNGEON—

—TODAY'S DELIVERANCE

The tales of living burial class with the worst of horrors. A few people now and then in the course of ages have lost their way in the Catacombs of Rome and even of Paris, and successive crowds of visitors still shudder at their fate.

Thus wrote the **Times** on the implications of the "living burial" at Hartley. The article went on to imagine the plight of the doomed 200. There they were six hundred feet below the light of day. It was death above, death below, and death around them, for out of the very walls of their prison they breathed a subtle poison.

How they lived, how they died, can only be conjectured.

But if the secret inside story of that dungeon could have been made known, how many personal and family tragedies might have been revealed ? Little fragmentary references in the press indicate poignant stories in plenty.

There was the case of George Hindmarch, aged 30, whose first day it was in that pit of death; there was Harry Clough, 47, who was likewise working his first shift; there was William Smith, a young glass-maker from Seaton Sluice, who had been persuaded to go down the pit as a visitor merely to have a look around! There was Jack Coyle, aged 28, of whom an obscure paragraph in the Newcastle **Courant** said :

We are requested to state for the information of his friends that John Coyle from Haswell, a married man with three children, went down the pit for the first time on the morning of the accident, and, of course, is amongst the sufferers.

What a story those few lines suggest! Had Jack gone from Haswell to Hartley to "better" himself ?

Then there were the numerous boys of tender age, about fifty or so of them. Three were from one family, the North

156

family. There was John, aged 14; Alexander, aged 12, and George, aged 10. What uncontrollable terror would fill the hearts and minds of these children in their dark and forbidding prison. It is significant that many of them were found nestling, tightly held for consolation, in the arms of their fathers.

Another tragic short story reported in the columns of the **Illustrated London News** (1.2.1862) concerned a widow who lay ill when the disaster occurred :

> There is one widow less than in the returns made for the relief fund. The wife of one of the lost men was very ill with consumption at the time her husband made his last fatal descent into the mine. As he did not return at the wonted time of finishing his shift, she got anxious about him, and after a day or two elapsed and no news of his release came, the fatal truth had to be told her. It was her death blow. She languished and died and on Sunday her remains were interred beside those of him she loved.

The conjectures about how the entombed men lived and died were in a small way answered by the written messages which were found on the bodies of some of the deceased. It was generally concluded that most, if not all the men were dead by Saturday, overcome by the gas. But that interval of time from Thursday morning until Saturday would be like an eternity.

The written messages are indeed moving. There was the record in Jim Amour's Overman's Report Book. Reid describes its having been written on "a common, thin, memorandum book, backed by a torn newspaper." The eager searchers, striving to find some evidence of a message from the dead, found on the last page, in a straggling handwriting the following record :

> Friday afternoon at half past two.
> Edward Armstrong, Thomas Gledstone, John Harding, Thomas Bell, and others, took extremely ill. We also held a prayer meeting at a quarter to two. Tibbs, Henry Sharp, J. Campbell, Henry Gibson, William Palmer—Tibbs exhorted to us again, H. Sharp also.

Two or three of those named as taking "extremely ill" were little boys.

Then there was the shot-box belonging to Jim Bewick. On this there was found to have been scratched :

Friday afternoon.

My Dear Sarah—I leave you—

Just a few scribbled words of love wrung from a strong man in his death agony.

On yet another man's box were found the words :

Mercy, O God!

An agonized exclamation, says Reid, which was but the expression of all the miners, as well as of those who sought to rescue them from their terrible fate.

What of the later life of the Hartley Pit ? Was the disaster the end of all coal-work there ?

As already indicated, immediately after all the drama of the pit-head when the bodies were recovered and decently interred, the pit was closed down. The noisy little steam-driven gins and lifting jacks and the rest, which had worked so hard during recent days, were silent now; the tumult and the shouting had died, the crowds dispersed, and the litter which they left was swept up. In effect the shutters were put up. The pit was dead.

But years later, the coal remaining to be worked when the pit so suddenly stopped was reached from another shaft.

After the disaster, T. E. Forster tells us, the Hartley royalty was abandoned by Messrs. Carr, but was subsequently leased to the owners of the Seaton Delaval Collieries by whom a fresh winning of the Yard Seam was made. This was done by means of the Hastings and Melton shafts, and work was resumed in 1877.

Operations were at that time limited to the Yard Seam—the level up to which the Hartley men had escaped in 1862. The shafts were however, afterwards deepened to the Low Main Seam and the old Hartley workings, drained of the flood waters, were entered once again in the year 1900.

What a ghostly picture would be beheld by the men who re-entered the seam after that lapse of time. As Mr. Forster says :

> The scene then presented was a strange and weird one. In many parts of the workings the tubs and gear were found standing ready as if for the resumption of the work which was so hurriedly abandoned more than 38 years previously.

158

Certainly on uncanny experience for the men who went into the seam again. The dripping wet workings, the dank, foisty air, the picks and shovels of the men who were lost, lying around here and there, the tangible skeleton-forms of drowned pit ponies, the intangible ghosts of men fleeing for their lives—all an unforgettable experience to those who were back in an underworld so haunted.

As to the half of the broken beam, the cause of all the trouble "it still lies buried" said Forster in 1912. And doubtless it is still there today, deep in the old Hester shaft.

The final stages of my researches into the Hartley story entailed, of necessity, my visiting Hartley and engaging in correspondence with people in that district who were likely to help me in my quest.

One afternoon in the summer of 1962, I set out alone to explore the area. It was a fine but blustery day. The first stop of interest was when I paused before reaching Hartley, to gaze upon the imposing facade of the famous Seaton Delaval Hall built by Sir John Vanbrugh. One's thoughts naturally turned to the Delaval family, the mining magnates who once dwelt here and ruled this neighbourhood.

The disaster village was not easy to locate, for despite its age it is still described as New Hartley. The pit-head, scene of the tragedy, proved still more elusive. I tried to pin-point the old landmarks which had been suggested by my reading, but all in vain. Where, for instance, was the old Methodist chapel which had been used as the temporary resting-place of the unknown dead? Doubtless it had been demolished long ago.

After a while I headed for Earsdon, four miles away. The Parish Church, conspicuously situated on a hill, was visible a long way off. As I got nearer, it appeared to be just as the artist of the "Illustrated London News" had sketched it one hundred years ago.

On my entering the church door a gale-force wind howled ominously about the building, and, imprinted on my memory, is the sound made by the wire mesh covers high up over the belfry openings which rattled violently, reminiscent of the wildness of the elements in "Wuthering Heights".

Out in the churchyard the trees tossed and swayed over the tombstones as if it were a winter's day. Nevertheless, it was a profoundly moving experience to stand beside the significant Disaster Memorial, for here, reading name after name of the dead, one recollected in tranquillity the full impact of the Hartley tragedy.

Back in Hartley I eventually found the site of the disaster pit-head. Surrounded by cottage gardens it was indeed a forgotten spot, inaccessible to travellers. To confirm my discovery I knocked on a cottage door and was answered by a man named George Carse with whom I conversed for a while.

Yes, that walled enclosure over there was indeed the place. See, set in the wall, the date-stone from the old engine-house . . .

The site of the famous battle for life and death looked sadly desolate and forlorn. Moss and weeds sprouted from crevices in the stone wall around the pit mouth, and the covers of garden-frames were disposed here and there against it. I took one or two photographs.

Mr. George Carse, I learned, had worked for forty years in the pits hereabouts, finishing as a deputy-overman at the Hartley Hastings Pit.

As we talked he showed me a significant document. It was a personal document and yet it was much more than that. It was something which marked the end of an important local era, covering centuries of coal production at Hartley, with all its varying fortunes. I copied it down as follows :—

	National Coal Board,
Mr. George Carse,	Northern (N and C) Division,
9, Hester Gardens,	No. 2 Area,
New Hartley.	6th February, 1959.

Dear Sir,

The Divisional Board have regretfully decided that Hartley Colliery must close on Friday, 20th February, 1959. On behalf of the Board I therefore give you four weeks' notice that your employment with the National Coal Board will terminate on 6th March, 1959.

Signed : ....

Manager, Hartley Colliery.

That letter meant that the end of a long road had been reached. The coal seams were exhausted. Now, so far as coal-work was concerned, it seemed that Hartley was nothing but a memory. But how full and profound that memory!

A week or two later in the course of another fact-finding tour I had tea and a long talk with my friends Mr. and Mrs. Forrest, then resident at Morpeth. Mr. Forrest was at that time Group Manager for some collieries near Hartley and readily assisted my research. As a matter of interest his wife happens to be a descendant of the famous Rt. Hon. Thomas Burt, M.P., who, for fifty years was a leader of the Northumberland Miners.

In furtherance of my quest Mr. Forrest took me over to Barmoor Colliery to meet Mr. J. Oliver Shepherd, Under-manager at Barmoor, and formerly Under-manager at the Hartley Hastings Pit. We talked in the Colliery Office at Barmoor. A man after my own heart, Mr. Shepherd valued all that appertained to the memory of the Hartley Disaster. Not only at that meeting but in subsequent correspondence he has helped my researches. Here are a few of the points which have emerged from our discussions and letters.

With the closing of the Hartley Hastings Pit in 1959, there is now no pit working in the Hartley area ; of the two shafts at Hartley, the Hastings was the downcast and the Melton the upcast ; holings from the Hastings Pit into the old disaster pit workings had been made over many years, commencing with those mentioned by Mr. T. E. Forster as taking place in 1900, and Mr. Shepherd had himself inspected some holings made in the Yard Seam during his time at the Hastings Pit. These, as was expected, revealed heavy roof falls in the old colliery work-ings but nothing of special interest ; the Hastings Arms public house to be seen in Hartley today is the one mentioned in the press reports of 1862, but some old standards assert that, in its time, the house has sold groceries and butcher-meat as well as beer.

Two other matters of interest I gleaned from Mr. Shepherd.

The first concerned the broken beam. There had, at one time, been a view held in Hartley, that the remaining half of the broken beam was dropped down the shaft, after the recovery of the bodies, to clear the obstruction remaining below the Yard Seam. Little credence, however, could be attached to that theory.

The second matter concerned the driving of a Drift with 204 steps. In order to save underground travelling time at the Hartley Hastings Pit, a Drift was sunk about 1928, in the neighbourhood of what is known above-ground as The Avenue. The Drift went down to the Main Coal Seam and had 204 steps. Since that is exactly the number of lives lost at Hartley, I naturally asked if there was any significance in the fact. "Pure coincidence" said Mr. Shepherd. But what a remarkable coincidence.

Thus our story of a Great Disaster draws to its close. It is surely an epic story worthy of remembrance.

Looking back from this year 1963, we can view in perspective that event of one hundred and one years ago. It stands out not from the point of view of numbers lost, as the worst disaster in mining history, but most certainly as one unparalleled, unique.

It is interesting to glance for a moment at the context of the times in which the tragedy became headline news. England was mourning the loss of Albert, the Prince Consort. Lord Shaftesbury, prompted by a Christian sense of values, was campaigning on behalf of the victims of the new order of things. He, it was said, "did more than any single man or Government to check the raw power of the new industrial system." Not far away from him in London, Karl Marx, "that angry and indomitable modern Moses" was carving out his own tablets of the law soon to be published in his famous work **Capital,** in which he elaborated his economic analyses based on the Materialist Conception of History and the existence of Class War. People little realised then how potent the gospel according to Marx was to become in a few more decades in certain parts of the world.

The newspapers which reported the Hartley Disaster also carried news of the progress of the American Civil War. At home, the coal-owners were all-powerful. Attempts at the formation of an enduring trade union amongst the miners had been ruthlessly crushed, and those familiar instruments of the bosses' power—the black lists, the sackings, the eviction from tied houses—all were applied at will. And despite repeated enquiry and exposure, children still worked in the mines long hours for a mere pittance.

From out of that setting the epic of Hartley shines like a beacon in a workaday world full of shadows. And that dungeon of death, which stirred the conscience of the nation also helped prepare the way for the deliverance from bondage which is today so widely enjoyed.

Yet the awareness of the indebtedness is not so widespread as it ought to be. To many people Hartley is but a faint echo of long ago. Old poems, old pictures, old souvenirs such as inscribed wine glasses, survive to hint in a vague way at some obscure tragedy. The old folk-tale of "Hart-lar", heard in one's youth, now lacks the full knowledge and the emotion it once had. Hence it was good to read that the Centenary of Hartley was marked in January 1962 by a special service at Earsdon Parish Church and by the flood-lighting of the memorial. But it is high time the world was told the story afresh. So the purpose of this book will be served if it throws a spotlight on that great event of a century ago.

The Hartley calamity remains one of the greatest true stories of tragedy and disaster which the industrial life of our country has ever known. It is difficult to summarize such an epic in a few concluding paragraphs.

That it led to mining legislation making compulsory the provision of two shafts or outlets to every pit was one great beneficial outcome. Another was the setting up of a miners' permanent relief fund, the necessity for which was forcibly brought home by the hundreds of dependants who would otherwise have been destitute.

Those ten days of January, 1862, were unforgettable by any standard. It was a period of reasonable hope; it was a period of black despair.

It was a period which, following the crashing down of the great beam, saw the battering of an iron cage with its frail human cargo, the "living burial" of two hundred human souls, and the later discovery of their bodies in one "Vast Golgotha".

It was a period of unending drama and crises, with an invading multitude of sightseers, and the holding of mass meetings and prayer-meetings ; it saw the ghastly spectacle of bodies hauled from the pit, of the assembly of a mountain of coffins, of an impressive funeral procession, and the uncovering of an acre of land in which to lay the rows of the dead. It saw the mounting indignation of the populace move a Parliament to remedial action.

And whilst, on the one hand, this catastrophe caused the wholesale destruction of a village, it was, on the other hand, responsible for the creation of an abiding memory. This memory is of a two fold nature, making manifest the nobility of the human spirit in the face of adversity. Firstly, it gave evidence of the devoted endurance of the relatives gathered at the pit-head, who watched and waited in silent anguish, loyally keeping their vigil day after day, their night-watches grimly illumined by the braziers of burning coal. Secondly, there was the undaunted courage of the sinkers, those hardy and resourceful sons of toil, whose bravery matched the hour, as they faced death, splendidly unafraid.

Such a period in our mining annals is surely deserving of thoughtful and respectful remembrance.

It has been said in more recent times that the **Manchester Guardian** under C. P. Scott, showed how to make righteousness readable. So did the **Times** in 1862.

It is to the credit of the **Times** that it rose to the occasion with a grandeur of expression and a sincere evaluation of the significance of the Hartley Disaster when it wrote :

> It is a spectacle and a thought to possess the mind of a nation. The worst horror of the lowest dungeon and the tyrant's oubliette was here done on the largest scale on meek and innocent sons of toil.

These humble toiling folk had committed no crime to justify so cruel a fate.

> They had aroused no suspicion, penned no libel, breathed no heresy, whispered no watchword, offended no Bourbon, scandalized no inquisition; yet here they were, a hundred Ugolinos and their sons, confronting one another in the jaws of a living death with a mutual embrace and a common hope of Heaven.

APPENDIX No. 1

Mr. J. Kenyon Blackwell's Report to the Home Secretary

COPY of Mr. BLACKWELL'S REPORT to the Secretary of State for the Home Department, respecting the ACCIDENT which occurred at the HARTLEY COLLIERY, in the County of *Northumberland*, on the 16th January, 1862.

Mr. *Blackwell* to Sir *G. Grey*, M.P.

Sir,   London, 15 February 1862.

I HAVE the honour to report, that in conformity to your instructions, I attended the adjourned inquest which was held on the 3rd, 4th, 5th and 6th days of this month, to inquire into the causes of death of those persons who lost their lives by the accident which occurred at the Hartley Colliery, in the county of Northumberland, on the 16th of January last.

The number of persons who perished on this occasion was 204, namely, four who were killed by the fall of materials in the shaft, or died subsequently in it from the injuries thus received ; one who was killed by falling out of the loop in which he was being drawn out of the shaft after the accident, and 199 who died in the inetrior of the pit.

There were eight persons in the winding-cage, which was being drawn up in the shaft at the time of the accident. This cage was, at the moment of its occurrence, rather more than half-way up the shaft. Of these persons three were subsequently drawn out from amidst the wreck of timber and other materials in the shaft, without serious injury, after remaining there about twelve hours.

The pumping-engine beam at the Hartley Pit, weighing more than forty tons, was found, after this accident, to have been broken through its centre. The broken half had fallen down the shaft, carrying with it in its descent parts of the pump spears, the buntons and collars retaining the pumps and the spears in their places, the brattice by which the shaft was divided, and portions of the timber-lining of the shaft.

A large part of the timber and other materials thus carried down was found to have been arrested near the yard-seam, at the depth of 138 yards from the surface, by the massive oak buntons upon which the middle set of pumps in the shaft stood.

Among this wreck, and upon it, fell masses of stone from the unwalled sides of the shaft, forming an accumulation by which the shaft was so completely closed that all communication between the internal air then filling the workings in the two lower seams of the pit and the external air above was entirely cut off.

Although the most strenuous efforts, directed by great practical skill, were made without intermission, notwithstanding the danger by which they were attended, to penetrate this obstruction in the shaft, this object was not accomplished until six days had elapsed after the occurrence of the accident, when every person then inclosed in the pit was found to have been long dead.

It appears to be certain, from the date of the entry in the book found on the person of the overman, Amour, that all those who were then in the pit must have died not later than the afternoon of the day succeeding this accident.

At the time of its occurrence there must have been a large quantity of fuel burning upon the grate of the ventilating furnace in the yard-seam in which the bodies were found.

Although it was proved that the fuel had been raked off the bars of this furnace before the death of those who were inclosed in the pit, it is probable, from the nature of the air found in the workings when the pit was re-entered, and from the comparatively early period at which death appears to have ensued, that this fuel continued to burn for some time after the accident, thus producing the intermixture of a large

165

volume of noxious gases with the air of the pit. In addition to this, the respiration of the 199 men and boys who died in the yard-seam, and of the 43 horses which were left in the low main-seam, below, would rapidly tend to render the air of the pit unfit for the support of life.

Since the loss of life on this occasion could not be averted, it is satisfactory to know that the death of the sufferers occurred early, and that it appears not to have been attended by much pain.

The Hartley pit was sunk about 17 years ago. The shaft is 12 feet 3 inches diameter; it is 200 yards in depth, namely 72 yards from the surface to the high-main seam; 66 yards from the high-main to the yard seam; 49 yards from the yard to the stone-drift leading to the workings in the low main-seam; and 13 yards from the stone-drift to the bottom of the sump.

The high-main seam at this pit had been exhausted by former workings; there are workings, but to a very limited extent, in the yard seam; the workings in progress at the time of this accident were almost exclusively in the low-main seam.

The shaft of the Hartley Pit had not been walled except for a short distance below the surface; under this the strata, where considered liable to give way, were secured by a lining of planks kept in their places by round timber cribs or curbs of from 4 to 5 inches scantling. These cribs were cleaded or sheeted toward the interior of the shaft with deal battens.

The shaft was divided through its centre, from east to west, by a timber brattice or partition formed of planks.

The northern half of the shaft was occupied by the bottom and middle sets of pumps, which were connected with the outside end of the pumping-engine beam.

This side of the shaft formed the upcast; the ventilating furnace drift, through which the return air from all the workings passed, entered the shaft on its north side in the yard seam.

The southern half of the shaft was occupied by the winding cages; it formed the downcast.

The top set of pumps occupied a staple or small shaft, situated under the inside or steam end of the pumping-engine beam, to which this set of pumps was connected.

The quantity of water at the Hartley Pit was very large; it found its way into the pit almost entirely through the workings in the low-main seam. The quantity amounted to from 1,400 to 1,500 gallons per minute.

From the level at which this water entered the pit it was necessary to raise it from the depth of 200 yards; to effect this required the use of great engine power.

There was a tract of old drowned workings on the low-main seam in the Hartley Royalty connected with a pit called the Mill Pit. Some time previously to the accident, exploring drifts from the Hartley Pit workings in the above seam had been carried towards this drowned tract, preceded by bore holes. The pound of water in the old workings had been tapped, and was running off through these holes at the period when this accident occurred.

The Inspector of Mines for the district ,recognising the danger to be apprehended at the Hartley Pit from a possible sudden influx of water, and for the improvement of the ventilation of the pit, had, during the period while these drifts were in progress, induced the proprietors to sink a staple from the yard to the low-main seam at a point where the latter was 14 yards higher than the mouth of the stone drift by which the workings in that seam were connected with the shaft; this staple was therefore, to some extent, out of the reach of water.

The Inspector had also procured the placing of a ladder in this staple, by which, after the accident, all those who were then in the low-main workings reached the yard-seam.

Unfortunately, above this seam where the obstruction in the shaft occurred, there was no other communication except that through the shaft itself for the distance of 66 yards, until the high-main seam was reached; to this latter seam there was separate access from the surface through the staple occupied by the top set of pumps.

APPENDIX ONE

The pumping-engine at this pit had a steam cylinder of 86¼ inches in diameter; the pressure of the steam used was 14 lbs. per square inch; the steam was condensed on both sides of the steam piston; the engine was of the estimated force of 300 horse-power.

The length of the beam of the engine was 34 feet 6 inches from centre to centre of the outside gudgeons; the sectional dimensions of each of the two sides of which it was composed, taken through the centre gudgeon-hole, were 8 feet in the vertical by 4¼ inches in the cross section, exclusive of the metal in the ribs and in the boss.

The centre gudgeon, forming the centre of motion of the beam, was situated 8 inches nearer to the outside or pumping end than the middle of the beam. Its stroke was thus 10 feet at the inside or steam end, and 9 feet 3 inches at the outside or pumping end, situated over the pit-shaft.

The pumps connected with this engine were divided into three sets. The bottom set, lifting the water from the sump in the shaft below the low main to the yard seam, was 52 yards, and the middle set, lifting from the yard to the high main seam, was 66 yards in height. These two sets of pumps and the spears connecting them with the outside end of the pumping-engine beam, were situated in the northern half of the shaft. They were both bucket sets. The buckets were 2 feet in diameter, working strokes of 9 feet 3 inches. The main dry spear, extending from the engine-beam to the top of the middle set of pumps, was 14 inches square. Below this point, from the Y to the top of the bottom set of pumps, it was 10 inches square. These spears were of Memel timber. The wood in the bottom dry spear, near the place where it had parted, was found to be not perfectly sound.

The bottom set of pumps stood on the bottom of the sump, that is, that portion of the shaft below the stone drift leading to the workings in the low-main seam.

The middle set stood upon oak buntons of great strength, which were placed side by side and in tiers over each other, extending nearly half-way across the shaft of the pit.

The top set of pumps, lifting from the high main seam to the surface, a height of 72 yards, was situated in the staple sunk to this seam, near the inside or steam end of the engine-beam. This set also, as the others, was a set of bucket pumps; the buckets were 2 feet 6 inches diameter, working a stroke of 6 feet 3 inches.

The weight of the dry and wet spears, of the buckets and of the columns of water in the bottom and middle sets of pumps lifted from the outside end of the pumping-engine beam, when the engine made its inside stroke, appears from calculation to have been about 55 tons.

The smaller weight of the top set in the staple, which was connected with the engine-beam on the opposite side of its centre of motion to the bottom and middle sets, was compensated by the difference in the length of the two ends of the engine-beam from the centre of motion, the weight of the steam-piston, piston-rod cross-head, and iron catch-pin attached to the beam.

The steam in this pumping engine being condensed on both sides of the piston, the speed with which it would travel through its inside and outside strokes would so long as the connexion of the beam with the pumps at each end was maintained, be equal; but this arrangement rendered this engine liable, in the event of the breakage of its connexion with the outside or inside set of pumps, and more particularly with the outside, to serious damage.

All the sets of pumps in connexion with this engine being bucket pumps, the entire resistance to its motion was accumulated alternately in opposite directions to the action of the steam, without any check to that action existing on the other side, and in the event of this resistance ceasing by the breakage of the pump connexions, it was inevitable that the engine should destroy itself, as, in fact, occurred.

In that class of engine termed the Cornish engine, which is most commonly employed where it is necessary that great power should be exerted in pumping, the same circumstances of danger as those which appear to have produced the accident at the Hartley Pit do not exist.

167

THE HARTLEY COLLIERY DISASTER, 1862

The steam in such engines is condensed on the under side of the piston only. The total force thus brought into action in the inside stroke is that only which is required to lift the spears and plungers of the pumps, without the additional weight of the column of water.

The descent of the spears and the plungers of the pumps by their own weight, after the steam has been readmitted to the under side of the piston, forces the column of water in the pumps to ascend. In such engines there is no danger of that loss of load from the breakage of the connexions with the pumps which appears to have destroyed the engine at the Hartley Pit.

The use of bucket pumps, of large dimensions, to form all the sets of pumps in connexion with a powerful pumping engine, is evidently a source of much danger.

In such cases having to lift at the same time, not only the weight of the spears but that also of the water resting upon the buckets, the tendency is to economise weight as much as possible, and consequently to reduce the dimensions of the spears by which the connexion of this weight with the engine is maintained.

There are special causes of breakage connected with the action of bucket pumps. The whole power of the engine must be applied to them as a direct strain tending to sever their connexion with the engine.

The buckets are liable to become fast in their working barrels from various causes, such as the bursting of a bucket-hoop, or the entrance into the pump of dirt along with the water.

The blast holes through which the water enters the pumps may become choked up with dirt, and this would throw an excessive strain on the spears.

It was proved that the sump at the bottom of the shaft of the Hartley Pit had not been cleansed out for a great length of time.

The timber forming the spears was probably rendered brittle by the elevated temperature of the pumping half of the shaft, which was used as the upcast.

That liability to breakage existed at this engine was proved by a former accident which occurred in 1858, when its speed was only 4½ strokes per minute instead of 7½ strokes, as at the period of this accident. On this occasion the main spear in the pumping shaft broke, and the connexion of the piston-rod with the engine-beam appears, in consequence, to have been nearly severed.

It was necessary under those circumstances which existed at the Hartley Pit, namely, the constant influx of large volumes of water, with the possibility of its increase, while there was only very limited standage room for it below the level of the pumps, that the bottom set should be bucket pumps, the buckets and clacks of which can be drawn out and replaced from above through the pumps, in case of their being temporarily overpowered by water; but the upper sets of pumps, namely, the middle set in the shaft connected with the outside end of the engine-beam, and the top set in the staple connected with the inside end, should have been plunger pumps; these two last sets being situated above the level to which it was probable that the water in the pit could rise.

This arrangement of the pumps would in all probability have prevented such an accident as that which occurred, since, under it, the entire resistance to the motion of the engine would not, as under that which was adopted, have been accumulated alternately in one direction and on one side only of the centre of motion of the engine-beam, during each stroke of the engine; but a balanced resistance on each side would have been presented to the action of the steam in whichever direction the piston might travel.

It appeared from the evidence of men who were being wound up in the shaft at the time of this accident, that a breakage of the spears in the shaft, by which the engine lost its load wholly or in part, did occur prior to the breakage of the beam and the fall of its broken half into the pit.

It appeared that when this breakage of the spears occurred the engine was commencing its inside stroke.

APPENDIX ONE

The resistance to the descent of the piston in the steam cylinder being thus removed, the piston would be carried downwards by the pressure of the steam on its upper surface augmented by the vacuum below, amounting to a force of about 62 tons, and would rapidly acquire momentum in its descent through a stroke of 10 feet in length, until both the piston and that end of the beam connected to it were suddenly arrested by the iron catch-pin fixed upon the beam, at that point, coming down upon the spring beams where they were rendered perfectly rigid in their resistance by vertical cast-iron columns which were firmly bolted to them beneath.

The engine-beam, the breakage of which was the immediate cause of the loss of life which resulted from this accident, was made of iron of fair quality.

It was of the full ordinary sectional dimensions of beams used in engines of similar power to this.

The over-wedging of the centre gudgeon of the beam, and the occurrence of severe frost at the time of the accident, may have contributed to render it somewhat more liable to fracture than it would otherwise have been, but these circumstances were not alone sufficient to account for this occurrence.

The beam had been at work under the load it was carrying for about seven years.

The breakage of the beam must be attributed to the violent concussion to which it was subjected, when it, together with the steam-piston connected to it, were suddenly arrested, after descending through a stroke of 10 feet with the velocity acquired under the pressure of the steam, by coming in contact with the spring beams beneath, after the counterbalancing load in the shaft was partially or wholly lost.

Notwithstanding the accident which occurred to this engine-beam, it cannot be disputed that cast-iron is a material the qualities of which give it great value in engineering construction, whilst its comparatively low cost has brought it into general use. Its fluidity at a low temperature enables it to take the form of any mould into which it may be run. Its stiffness when cold, and even its bulk and weight, are qualities which contribute to its value in many situations.

The defects of this material may in almost all cases be guarded against, and in particular when applied to engine-beams, by a judicious combination of wrought iron in the construction. If the sides of the beam which broke at the Hartley Pit had been trussed with wrought iron rods 2½ or 3 inches in diameter, applied to the upper and under-edges of each of the sides of which this beam was formed, it would in all probability have sustained the effects even of the violent concussion to which it was subjected, and had the beam broken under the concussion, no part of it certainly would have fallen into the shaft.

Shafts similar to that of the Hartley Pit over which pumping-engine beams are at work, might, without any considerable outlay, be so fenced that, even in the event of breakage occurring to a beam, no part of it could fall into the shaft.

The timber lining which was used in the weakest parts of the Hartley shaft to retain the strata in their places, did not prevent them from falling in after this accident to a considerable extent.

The principal fall took place at a point about 30 feet above the yard-seam, where the shaft was crossed by a trouble or fault, and where probably the strata had been still further weakened by the action of the ventilating furnace which was in the yard-seam.

The sides of the shaft gave way at this point to the width of nearly 30 feet, and the masses of stone which fell at the period of the accident or shortly after, and which continued to fall during the whole time whilst the sinkers were engaged in endeavouring to reach the yard-seam, were a source of great danger and delay in its accomplishment.

It is indisputable that the working of mines of any description through a single shaft, introduces an element of serious additional danger into such operations.

In those cases in which furnace ventilation is employed in connexion with a single bratticed shaft, the quantity of air passing through the pit must necessarily be restricted, as the heat of the furnace cannot be raised without danger of firing the brattice.

Single shafts lined and bratticed with timber are used in some districts in this country, where no adequate reason can be alleged for adopting them, the depth in the districts now referred to being small, the strata to be passed through being easy to penetrate, and the position of the minerals to be reached being well known.

In other districts where large and unexplored tracts of minerals have to be won at great depths, where rocks of extreme hardness, or other strata presenting great difficulties in their penetration, have to be passed through, where immense volumes of water have to be encountered and stopped back by tubbing, and where the outlay attendant on such operations is proportionately large, the results of this outlay being at the same time uncertain, it cannot be surprising that a system should be adopted, in some instances, which is attended by a considerable diminution in the outlay to be sustained, and not presenting more than a remote and contingent chance of extra exposure of the persons engaged to those dangers which are, after all, inseparable from mining operations.

The cost of the labour and materials required for the sinking of two shafts in a new winning in place of one shaft, the sectional area of the two taken together being equal to that of the single shaft, may be estimated to involve an additional expenditure of from 10 to 25 per cent., according to the depth, the nature of the strata, and he quantities of water which have to be passed through.

The actual amount of this extra outlay would, however, vary from trivial to very large sums. In most cases, the difference in cost ought certainly not to be regarded; but if new winnings were again to be made of the same expensive character as some existing examples, in which 500, 600, or 700 yards in depth of strata have been sunk through, under the most formidable difficulties, and at enormous cost, it appears questionable whether the additional outlay necessary to provide two shafts in place of the single one, by which these great depths have hitherto in every case been attained, would not impede the development of such enterprises. The evils and dangers arising from the use of single shafts in mining oprations have, however, been already so fully acknowledged, and have been rendered so evident by this recent accident, that it appears desirable that such a system should not in future be permitted.

With regard to mines now in operation the difficulty of arriving at a just conclusion appears greater.

In those deep mines worked by a single shaft, where large quantities of water have been stopped back by tubbing, and where the strata present unusual difficulties to their penetration, the sinking of a second shaft of even the smallest diameter would involve a most serious outlay; and since these deep, difficult, and originally costly winnings are frequently those which are the least profitable in a commercial point of view, it is probable that the effect of any legislative enactment, enforcing such an additional outlay as the necessary condition of such mines continuing to work, would be to cause their stoppage, and to throw out of employment a large number of the mining population.

I have, &c.
(signed) *J. Kenyon Blackwell.*

APPENDIX No. 2

Dr. Davison's Letter to the 'Lancet'

THE LATE CALAMITY AT NEW HARTLEY.

To the Editor of the Lancet.

SIR,—In your journal for March 1st there were some remarks relative to the late unfortunate calamity at Hartley Colliery; and as the conclusions were different from those I had given, I hope you will insert the following observations on the effects of the gas, and my reasons for stating that the gas was carbonic oxide.

On ascertaining the extent of the accident, the number of men and boys down the mine, and that it would be some time before they could be communicated with, our first anxiety was whether there would be a sufficient supply of air and water, when we were assured there would be sufficient for some days. The medical men also gave as their opinion that there would be no fear of starvation for some time, as many of the men who went down last would have some food with them; there was also a quantity of oats, and they could get at some of the ponies. Matters went on pretty well during the following day (Friday, Jan. 17th), or at least the early part of it, as there were distinct answers from the men below to the signals given by the men in the shaft. The sinkers imagined they heard signals on Sunday, the 19th; but as the last written record of any being alive was poor Amour's journal, dated "Friday, quarter to two," it must have been a mistake. On Sunday, smells began to be felt in the shaft; on Monday, they became decidedly unpleasant; and great anxiety was felt when David Wilkinson, one of the men, came to bank very much affected with some gas which he stated was coming through the obstruction in the shaft. And on a hole being forced through, great quantities of gas came off, affecting the men very much; many were seriously ill, but none completely insensible. Mr. Coulson going down, he found the gas rising in the pit to a great height. Now, as there had not been any means used for ventilating the shaft, this proves it was lighter than the atmospheric air; and on a candle being put down, it burned, if anything, brighter and clearer and though the men suffered so much, their candles never went out, clearly proving that it was a gas very *injurious* to life, though supporting combustion in a certain degree when mixed with common air; whereas in a mixture of carbonic acid gas and air the candles are always *extinguished* before the men suffer much from its effects. The only other gas generated in a coal mine is carburetted hydrogen, which explodes by a candle when mixed with air, though the men can work *in it* with a Davy lamp;—thus, I think, proving that it was neither carbonic acid nor carburetted hydrogen gas. The question is, what gas was it ? Judging from the effects on the men, its lightness, and its supporting combustion when mixed with air, I think it must have been carbonic oxide gas— certainly not a natural product of the mine, but most likely formed at the furnace. On this question I shall not dilate, as my friend, Mr. George Baker Forster, has brought the subject before the Mining Institute where it will be fully discussed; but I wish to give an explanation regarding the evidence I gave before the Coroner. When Mr. Blackwell told me that the fire had been raked out, I ought to have added that the coal-ashes, &c., would fall below the bars, where they would smoulder for some time, the heat from which, together with that from the furnace bars and plates, must have been great, and have tended, in a confined space, to keep up a slow but imperfect combustion, the product of which would be carbonic oxide gas, and which caused the death of the poor men.

171

THE HARTLEY COLLIERY DISASTER, 1862

I shall now give the symptoms which the men laboured under who were working in the shaft, of whom a great many were affected from Monday night till the bodies were found; and I think there can be only one opinion of the heroic devotion of my friend, Mr. Coulson, and the fine fellows under him, in returning again and again to their work after suffering so severely as some of them did.

1st Class.—The men were very little affected *in the shaft*, and came to bank in the loop without being tied in to prevent their falling out; and when they came to the fresh air they were still able to walk to the cabin, about ten yards off, without assistance. They then began to feel giddy, with frontal headache, tremours in the lower extremities, and sometimes sickness; but on giving them strong tea (of which there was always some ready), with a very small quantity of whisky, they were soon able to change their clothes, walk to their lodgings, about 600 yards off, and in three or four hours resume their work.

2nd Class.—The men felt the effects of the gas at the *bottom of the shaft*, but were able to come to bank without any assistance, as in Class 1; but immediately they came in contact with the fresh air, the tremors, debility, and sickness increased very much, causing them to stagger and require assistance to prevent their falling down; were quite sensible, answered rationally, but did not like to be disturbed. On dashing cold water freely over the temples and face, administering hot tea with whisky, &c., they were soon relieved, but experienced frontal headache for an hour or two, felt inclined to vomit, and complaining of something lying at the stomach; others that there was something constantly moving up and down in the stomach. In about an hour they were able to walk to their lodgings, and in five or six hours resume their work. They stated they could not have lived long in the shaft.

3rd Class.—The men were so suddenly affected by the gas coming up the hole in the shaft as to require the assistance of their comrades to lash them to the loop to prevent them falling out. One man incautiously put his head into the hole, when he was observed to drop, and lay there till his comrade came down the shaft, about sixty yards, when he lashed him in the loop, and sent him to bank, where he was found in a slight state of syncope. On the usual remedies being applied, he soon rallied so far as to answer questions; complained of coldness, sickness, headache, with great debility, pulse almost imperceptible; but in a short time he was able to be led to his lodgings. Mr. Wm. Coulson, jun., was brought up in a similar state; but the symptoms continued longer, requiring quietness, rest, &c.; but in about an hour he was able to answer questions, and give his father an account of the state of the shaft. Another man was very violent and excited, wishing to fight the medical men in attendance—very much like the effects of chloroform. Others suffered in a state between Classes 2 and 3. Adams and Wilson (who first went in where the dead bodies were, "and who stated that their candles burned brightly and clearly, thus proving that it was not carbonic acid gas given off by the men themselves,") also Humble and Hall, viewers, who followed them, suffered very much; and Mr. Humble stated, if he had not been assisted he must have dropped there. None of them were completely insensible.

GAS EFFECT ON MEN IN PIT

I will now give the appearances of the bodies as they were brought to bank; but as no post-mortem examination was ordered by the Coroner, the examination was only superficial. For clearness, I shall divide them into different classes.

The first class did not present any unusual appearance; bodies flaccid, face and lips pale, as well as the whole cutaneous surface; eyelids open in a few instances, but generally closed; sunk in the orbit; cornea opaque and soft. About twenty bodies were in this class, and were easily recognised.

APPENDIX TWO

In the second class (comprising by far the greatest number) the bodies were slightly swollen and relaxed, the arms and fingers bent and rigid, the skin of the palm of the hand sodden as if immersed in water, and the eyes sunk and dim. In various parts of the body the skin presented patches of a bright appearance, occasionally intermingled with streaks of a paler colour. In some instances a bloody fluid, of a bright red colour, oozed from the mouth and nostrils, and I may observe that the men noticed this down the pit. Many of these bodies were recognised with difficulty.

In the third class the head and face were greatly swollen, the features distorted, &c., fluid from the mouth dark and red; eyes prominent and somewhat reddened; abdomen much distended with gas, &c., strong odours from the bodies; patches of a red colour observed on various parts. This class embraced but a smaller number, and they were found near the furnace; the skin of two of the bodies was charred in several places.

As there was not any of the gas taken for analysis, and none of the bodies examined, we can only come to a conclusion as to what the gas was from its general character, its effects on the men, candles, &c., and these combined point to carbonic oxide gas as the cause of the death of the men. To account for the different appearances of the bodies, their position and the part of the mine where they were found must be taken into account, as some parts were much hotter than others.

I have to express my obligations to Messrs. M'Alister, Lambert, and Weddell, for assisting me from their notes in giving the symptoms, &c. I desire also to thank you on behalf of my medical brethren for your kind observations on our conduct in connexion with the melancholy accident.

I am, Sir, your obedient servant,

A. DAVISON, L.R.C.S. Ed.

Hastings Cottage, Seaton Delaval, Newcastle-on-Tyne,
     March, 1862.

APPENDIX No. 3

HEROES OF HARTLEY

At the Social Occasion held 20th May, 1862, to honour the Hartley Sinkers, payments were made to the men on the basis of the hours each spent in the shaft as follows:

Name	Payment	Name	Payment
Wm. Coulson	Not stated	Ralph Heron	£19
Wm. Coulson, Jnr.	,,	Lashley Hope	£13
George Emmerson	£30	William Johnson	£7
William Shield	£30	Richard Johnson	£17
David Wilkinson	£30	Peter Lindsay	£14
John Angus	£8	John Little	£17
John Burns	£14	R. Maughan	£16
Mitchell Bailey	£6	John Manderson	£11
Fenwick Charlton	£6	Robert Milburne	£5
Matthew Chapman	£14	James Muters	£14
Edward Davison	£15	John Nevins	£4
Matthew Dodds	£16	George Pace	£11
George Graham	£8	William Reed	£19
John Henderson	£10	John Smith	£17
Thomas Hetherington	£6	Henry Snowden	£17
Ralph Harrison	£14	John Sedgwick	£13
Robert Hamilton	£4	Andrew Swaine	£19
John Heron	£18	Jesse Smith	£5
Elsdon Heron	£19	Robert Wilson	£16

Newcastle **Courant,** 23rd May, 1862.

174

APPENDIX No. 4

Copy of Circular Issued by the Home Secretary in consequence of the Hartley Disaster

CIRCULAR addressed to the INSPECTORS of COAL MINES.

(*N.B.*—This Circular was substituted for one on the same subject sent on the 24th Jan.,)

Sir,
Whitehall, 28 January 1862.

I AM directed by Secretary Sir George Grey to request that you will at your earliest convenience transmit to him a return, so far as relates to your district, showing —

1st. The number of accidents, distinguishing fatal and non-fatal, arising from the falling in of shafts, or obstruction of the same, during each of the last three years.

2nd. The number of collieries or iron-stone mines having single shafts, and the number having double shafts.

3rd. The possibility of effecting communications under-ground between adjacent works belonging to the same or different proprietors, so as to obtain the advantage of their respective shafts.

4th. The practicability of having double shafts in every instance, and the probable cost thereof.

I am, &c.

(signed)   G. Clive.

Home Office Papers.

175

INDEX